EXOSOMES
Songs of Healing

By

Ed Park, MD

Los Angeles
Pileus Productions
2023

Library of Congress Cataloging-In-Publication Data

Names: Park, Edward (Dr.) author
Title: Exosomes — Songs of Healing / Ed Park, MD
Description: Pileus Productions, Los Angeles, California (2023)
Identifiers: LCCN 2027076345 | ISBN 978-0-9826063-2-2 (paperback)
Subjects: LCSH: Exosomes | Extracellular Vesicles | Aging- Molecular aspects | HEALTH AND FITNESS/ Alternative Therapies | MEDICAL/Genetics

Paperback ISBN 978-0-9826063-2-2
10 9 8 7 6 5 4 3 2 1

1st Edition, November 2023

Also available as:
E-Book | ISBN: 978-0-9826063-3-9
Audiobook | ISBN: 978-0-9826063-4-6

Printed on Demand by Kindle Direct Publishing.

ENDORSEMENTS

This book is a must for any regenerative medicine specialist as it reviews the fundamentals of the disease of aging at the cellular, epigenetic, and genetic levels in a way I have never seen before.

Vince Giampapa, MD
Founder of A4M and CEO RMI-institute

Dr. Park's new book on exosomes is a must-read! I have the APOE 4/4 variant genotype. Each time Dr. Park has administered the treatment, my thinking becomes clearer and sharper."

John Asher,
CEO Asher Longevity Inst.

Dr. Park is a personal friend and an "outside-the-box" practitioner we need in order to shift to a whole new level of awareness. To keep things fun and comprehensive, he uses metaphors, diagrams, storytelling, and references to common, everyday things and processes to explain complicated biology.

Vincent Spano,
Actor, Writer, Producer

Songs of Healing is a peek into the future. I am a walking (literally) example of the results of exosome therapy. My story is in the book and my results have turned me into an evangelist. It's thoughtfully, beautifully, and sometimes humorously written for all by a wonderful, altruistic man whose life mission shifted midstream to help give birth to a hidden healing force within us all. Say hello to the child of the future.

Bob Johnson, Patient

I received 3 COVID vaccines and then got COVID twice last year. I was experiencing dizzy spells, heart palpitations, and fainted several times. We met, spent some time together, and you gave me my first nasal treatment. The sleep, the energy, headaches, lightheadedness...all of it had either improved so dramatically or disappeared altogether. Please don't stop doing what you do, Dr. Park. People need you more than they know.

Carren Seidel, Patient

Table of Content

Table of Figures

PROLOGUE

I want to thank you for picking up this book. I have three goals that I want us to collaborate on: to learn about exosomes, to understand cell biology more deeply, and to provide some hope for reversing aging and maintaining health. The simple message of the book is that stem cell-derived exosomes are a normal way your body repairs and now we can use them to help you.

This is my third non-fiction book. My first was called *"Telomere Timebombs- Defusing the Terror of Aging"*, which explains the basic engine of aging and illness: telomere erosion in stem cells. My second non-fiction book, *"The Telomere Miracle"*, was published by Hay House, and explains human physiology and health through the activation of telomerase using healthy habits.

In this third book, I hope you will be entertained, fascinated, and encouraged about the prospects of staying healthier for longer. I hope my writing style, which is conversational and uses the minimum necessary scientific jargon, will be pleasing to your mind's ear. After years of blogging and even writing screenplays, I try to write using analogies and try not to sound too serious.

I made a simple error about RNA in my first book that most readers would not ever find. I don't think that it invalidated the rest of the book, but one reviewer begged to differ.

That's okay. It is my intention to share only the simplest, known scientific truths here, without error. I may not succeed 100% due to my own error or perhaps because science is always under revision. Where appropriate, I will use citations of articles but if I've left them out, it should be safe to assume that I am simply repeating common scientific knowledge.

Finally, throughout the book you will find citations that you can look up in the endnotes by chapter and then the superscripted number. Some of them will be scientific articles. Others may be hyperlinks to web pages, including blogs or videos that I have made. If you want to know more, a more comprehensive listing of some of my web content can be found after the book in APPENDIX A that follows the main chapters. If you are interested in training to use exosomes clinically, see APPENDIX B.

Chapter 1

A WHOLE NEW PARADIGM

Dare to be naïve

—Buckminster Fuller

I wrote this book because there are currently no other books in the lay press to explain that exosomes are a relatively new discovery and the fundamental way that cells communicate and repair the body in lab animals and, apparently, in humans, too.

I often am asked, "What is the difference between exosomes and stem cells?" That question would be like asking, "What is the difference between language and people?" You see, language is what people use to communicate with and influence other people. You would never confuse a person, who is an autonomous and self-sufficient entity, with their speech or writing whose significance depends upon the speaker/writer and the listener/reader.

In journalism, they talk about "The W's": who, what, where, when, and why. In this year of 2023, a movie won many Academy Awards and had a very ambitious title that addressed some of these questions; it was called *Everything, Everywhere, All at Once*. That is an excellent frame of mind to consider why we need to understand exosomes.

In the evolution of science itself, we find what Professor Stephen Jay Gould called "punctuated equilibrium." Briefly, that means that everything mostly stays the same for long periods until things suddenly change. Humanist prophet Buckminster Fuller said, "You never change things by fighting the existing reality. To change something, build a new model that makes the existing model obsolete." Both sentiments apply when we consider the field of exosomes. When you look at high school biology textbooks from when you were in school, there is this glaring error in the cartoons of a cell and its functioning. Although some obscure scientists had an inkling of a system of exosome communication before, it wasn't until about 2009 that scientists began to realize that their protein-excreting model of cell biology was fundamentally incomplete. The old textbooks show proteins being excreted like this:

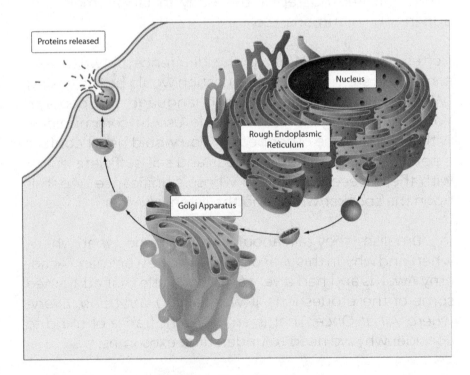

1.1: Old model of Cell Communication

What I am suggesting to you is that exosomes are the *sine qua non* of cell biology. Unlike the previous cartoon showing proteins being excreted out of cells and doing most of the cell communication, it is usually the cells' exosomes that are being sent out. In terms of cell communication, they are *everything*, they are *everywhere*, and their actions are occurring *all at once*. All plant and animal cells don't primarily rely on free proteins and direct contact to communicate with other cells; they use exosomes.

How did this misunderstanding happen, and will it ever be corrected? Like any other dogma, it is slow to change unless and until an alternative theory is invented and then replaces the old dogma. Cell biologists observed down to the level of electron microscopy and had robust ideas of how the inner workings of the cell take place. Look again at the cartoon, and you will see that we "knew" about the nucleus, which houses the blueprints of DNA. We "knew" about the endoplasmic reticulum, where ribosomes translate mRNA into proteins. We "knew" about the Golgi apparatus for packaging bubbles. But we didn't "know," despite our lying eyes seeing them on electron microscopy, that the mainstay of cell-to-cell communication is these tiny bubbles, which are extruded into the outside world. Scientists preferred to believe that the observed exosomes were cellular "poop" rather than cell communication because nobody imagined such a massive paradigm shift. This misconception would be like saying human language, such as speech, singing, and writing, is merely excreting poop. While we all know folks who lend credence to that idea, most would concede that language serves a loftier function than mere waste excretion. Below is how the cartoon will look in future textbooks. It shows that the **multivesicular endosome (MVE)** is like a shuttle bus for the batches of exosomes to reach the cell surface for extrusion.

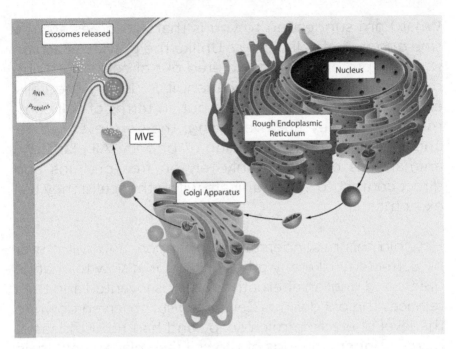

1.2: New Exosome Model of Cell Communication

THE PHOSPHOLIPID BILAYER

A fundamental concept to understand is the phospholipid bilayer. I know it sounds complicated, but it couldn't be simpler if you think about soap bubbles, which are often phospholipid molecules themselves. In chemistry, things tend to be hydrophobic and non-polar, or they are hydrophilic and polar. Think of oil floating atop the vinegar in salad dressing. If something is fatty, oily, or non-polar, it separates from watery solutions that are polar. All our cells are surrounded by these phospholipid bilayers, which have polar ends facing the watery solutions inside and outside the cell and their fatty tails facing each other in the middle. Exosomes are just tiny spheres made of phospholipid bilayers.

If you remember playing with soap bubbles, you know they can merge into each other. That is the way exosomes help

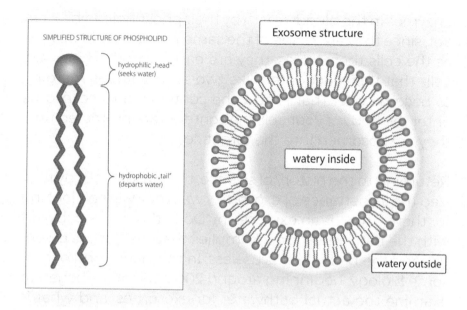

SIMPLIFIED STRUCTURE OF PHOSPHOLIPID

hydrophilic „head"
(seeks water)

hydrophobic „tail"
(departs water)

Exosome structure

watery inside

watery outside

1.3: Phospholipid Bilayers

cells influence each other. As a cell, if I want to change the behavior of another cell, I could use a signal like a protein, if the receptors exist, for that protein to trigger a response on the surface of your cell membrane. Some of these would include insulin, neurotransmitters like dopamine, and common signals for the immune system.

For the other 11,000+ known proteins in the human genome, the natural way for me as a cell to influence you, as another cell, is to create exosomes filled with proteins, messenger RNA to make proteins, and micro-RNA to block specific **protein translation**. More on translation later.

Exosomes are tiny 100-nanometer phospholipid balls made in the Golgi apparatus and sent out like messages in a glass bottle. For comparison's sake, cells are around 30,000 nanometers or 300 times the diameter. Exosomes are protected from the toxins, oxidants, and protein or RNA-degrading enzymes in the bloodstream by their phospholipid bilayers. Yet, since they are made of the same phospholipid bilayers as the cells themselves, they are easily absorbed into any cells that they encounter- like two soap bubbles merging to become one. That is how the contents of my exosome enter the body of your cell; the contents are protected until they are absorbed into the target cell.

Returning to the history of science, the reason nobody realized the importance of exosomes was they weren't looking for them. There is an expression, "Don't throw the baby out with the bathwater," which implies that the baby is essential, and the bathwater is useless. In this new world of exosome biology, beginning around 2009, scientists began to examine the actual bathwater for exosomes, and what is now emerging is this new paradigm. Some scientists will remain stuck in their dogma because they don't want to reimagine how cell biology works, so they will continue to focus on cells and proteins. But the cellular "poop," or exosomes, is how most cell communication is likely taking place, so scientists were wrongly throwing the bathwater out and only looking for proteins they already knew played roles.

1.4: DO Throw the baby out and KEEP the bathwater!

NOT ALL EXTRACELLULAR VESICLES ARE EXOSOMES

Like not all fruits are apples, but all apples are fruit, exosomes are a subclass of extracellular vesicles. Extracellular vesicles are all surrounded by phospholipid bilayers, and they come in at least three broad types, all smaller than most cells, and represent three different processes. Firstly, there are often large, **apoptotic bodies** that are fragments

of destroyed cells, like chunks of derelict spaceships floating in zero gravity after a space battle. They can be any size
and up to 5000 nanometers (nm).

Secondly, there are intermediate-sized **microvesicles,**
which are 100 to 1000 nm in diameter and represent a cell's
ability to gulp in or belch out using self-contained bubbles
created by pinching in (endocytosis) or budding out (exocytosis) of the phospholipid surface of the cell.

Thirdly, the smaller extracellular vesicles are what most scientists call **exosomes,** and they are too small at 100nm to
see in the cartoon below. They are purposefully made for cell
communication by the Golgi apparatuses and released as
batches of bubbles in another bubble known as a **multivesicular endosome or multivesicular body (MVE or MVB).**
The MVE provides a shuttle bus from the Golgi apparatus
to the cell's surface, where the exosomes are released into
the world outside the cell.

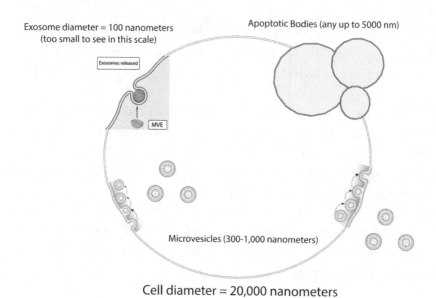

1.5: Size comparison of Three Types of Extracellular Vesicles

WHY DIDN'T WE KNOW ABOUT EXOSOMES?

It isn't that the scientists were stupid; they were just resistant to shift paradigms. Their electron microscopes visualized the multivesicular endosomes (bubbles with many exosomes inside) and saw them extruded from the cell surfaces. Instead of reimagining cell biology, they concluded that these tiny bubbles were "poop" because no one dared imagine that they were the primary means of cell-to-cell communication.

In fairness, it is easy to ignore something no one believes in. However, the ability to see, isolate, and analyze these exosomes was already in place. They just needed to save the bathwater, use mechanical techniques to isolate them, find the best soaps to dissolve the phospholipid bilayers, and then identify and quantify the proteins and RNA inside them.

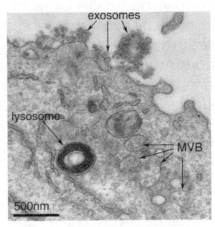

1.6: Electron Micrograph of exosomes[1] (MVB = MVE)

Now that we live in an emerging and radically different paradigm, the evolution of cell biology is accelerating, as with Stephen Jay Gould's model of sudden evolution or Buckminster Fuller's new paradigm rendering the old "proteins in solution" model of cellular communication obsolete. This is a significant change in studying cell biology, and our understanding of disease and wellness will be better served because of this shift to an exosome-based theory of cell communication.

NEW ANALOGY: EXOSOMES AS MUSIC

I said that exosomes are to cells as language is to human beings. If I may, I would like to adjust that analogy slightly to a subset of communication that serves us even better: music is to humans as exosomes are to cells. The reason for this shift is that while the contents of exosomes can be precisely identified and even quantified with technology, the significance of these "songs" is probably impossible to understand with standard scientific, deductive, and reductionist thinking.

What is the meaning of any word? The field of semiotics tells us that words can function both as signifiers (something literal) but also as the signified (or more profound concepts or meanings). Likewise, an expression or suppression of a specific protein might have different meanings depending on the other co-expressed proteins, the recipient cell's internal state, and the current ecological milieu of those cells.

Perhaps a better analogy would be to ask, what is the meaning of F sharp (F#)? You might say it is a multiple of (488hz) or the root note in Irving Berlin's favored key to compose and play in. But if you quantified the number of F#'s in "White Christmas" or Stravinsky's "The iRite of Spring," you would be no closer to understanding the music, the dance, the emotions, or the shift in consciousness for the listeners of those songs.

I can tell you that most of a particular stem cell type might tend to produce this amount of this specific mRNA to produce that particular protein, and therefore, I understand the who, what, where, when, and why of how one cell's exosome music makes another cell dance. But you would be foolish to believe me. We need to embrace the complexity and "dare to be naïve."

When I attended a lecture by Neil Turok, the director emeritus of the Perimeter Institute of Theoretical Physics, he said the workings of the universe can be summed up in a single equation shown below. Although I have real doubts about this claim, I don't question his second statement, which was that cell biology is the most complex thing imaginable.

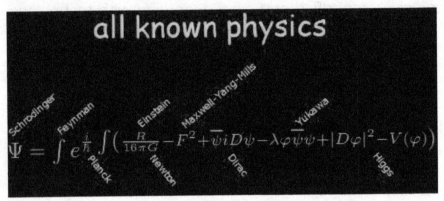

1.7: Neil Turok's equation for all known physics [2]

If we attempt to use reductionism and deductive reasoning to try to understand cell biology, we are doomed to failure. But if we accept failure from the start, we can use observation and intuition to garner some wisdom regarding the specific instances of F#s and related notes as to how they alter "consciousness" in other cells. We may someday develop some musical theories to help us appreciate the microcosmic dance of cell biology, but for now, it is quite a challenge.

Think of cell biologists as wrong-sized interdimensional beings without ears to hear or legs to dance to the music of exosomes. If actual interdimensional beings like that came to our world and found themselves with access to catalogs of music, whether they be on 8-track, vinyl, or packets traveling across the internet to computers, they could still get humans to feel something and get up and dance just by playing music they themselves couldn't hear. By studying exosome contents from particular cell types and their relative frequencies, scientists hope to infer, through inductive reasoning, some fundamentals about cellular music theory. Which proteins are expressed and repressed by the contents of the exosomes will help to understand scales, chords, meters, and genres of cell music.

In the grand scheme of things, we are those interdimensional aliens, totally "square" to the nature of the cellular music being played and heard. But that doesn't mean we can't keep finding and spinning those tunes to make those cells dance. Now that we accept our ignorance and embrace the challenge of becoming better at an impossible task, we are in the proper mindset to continue our journey toward a better understanding of how exosomes constitute songs of healing.

Chapter 2

A CRASH COURSE IN CELL BIOLOGY

I am still learning.

—Michelangelo, age 87

In this chapter, we will try to understand some essential elements of cell biology so that we can meaningfully discuss why we age and get sick. We will also hint at the coming revolution in both diagnostic and therapeutic medicine that is rapidly emerging. The key concepts we will discuss involve cell protein manufacturing, stemness and differentiation, gene activation and silencing via something called epigenetics, stem cell mutation and depletion, and gene therapies.

As I mentioned in the last chapter, scientists thought that the multivesicular endosomes, or bags of bubbles (i.e. exosomes), were releasing cellular "poop" or excrement. Not only was that assumption mistaken, but they also missed out on an earlier start to this thought revolution.

Teleologically speaking (i.e., working backwards from the conclusion to the causation), it would be complex and burdensome to have every significant protein require a specific cell surface receptor to have an effect on the internal workings of a cell. Instead, it would be easier and more elegant to make an exosome with cargo that is injected into the recipient cell, and then that cargo can't help but have its actions once it enters the target cell. I know that I promised to keep the scientific jargon to a minimum, but unfortunately, what follows in this chapter is the bare minimum of what we need to fully grasp this book.

Believe it or not, there is something called "The Central Dogma of Biology" which states that most of cell biology emerges from two main processes: *transcription* of the DNA genes (letter-for-letter recipes of DNA for creating proteins) into a **messenger RNA** (mRNA), and the *translation* of that mRNA recipe into a letter-for-letter amino acid chain which is a **protein**. There are details of this process that you don't really need to understand, but what is essential to know is that the transcription of the DNA takes place in the nucleus of the cell, where the library of chromosomes is kept, and that the translation of the mRNA recipe takes place outside the nucleus but inside the walls of the cell. This "sea inside" is called the cytoplasm and is watery like the sea outside. All the machinery and ingredients to make the proteins, mainly the amino acids and **transfer RNA (tRNA)**, are in the cytoplasm but they tend to be partitioned off in their own membrane-bound structures.

In this cytoplasm, which is defined as outside the nucleus's phospholipid bilayer but inside the outer cell wall's phospholipid bilayer, are the pleated areas with many beads of ribosomes on them known as the endoplasmic reticulum. "Rete" is Latin for net and the folded areas are studded with the machinery for protein translation known as ribosomes.

Ribosomes are made up of two subunits, which form a top and bottom, like a hamburger bun. The mRNA feeds through like mayo-covered bacon as it's being "translated." Ribosomes serve to "read" the single-stranded mRNA

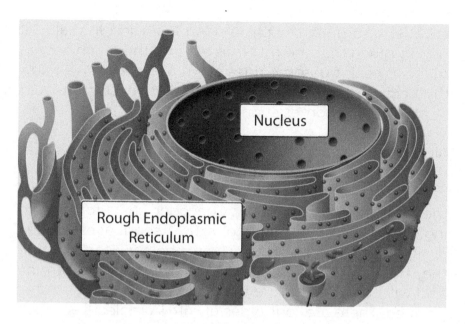

2.1: Rough Endoplasmic Reticulum

mRNA TO PROTEIN TRANSLATION

We will skip the copying of the DNA cookbook into mRNA recipes (transcription) and jump to the actual "cooking" of the proteins (mRNA translation). For this mRNA translation, we only need three things: the recipe (mRNA), the reading/writing machinery (two "hamburger buns" of the ribosomes), and the 21 flavors of amino acids being carried along with the 21 specific transfer RNAs (tRNA). All of life on Earth emerges from these 21 amino acids being assembled into proteins. Due to a lack of enzymes, humans can't make nine of them, which are therefore ingested in our diet and referred to as "essential amino acids."

As shown in the cartoon below, the ribosomes that are studding the surface of the rough endoplasmic reticulum are fed the mRNA transcript, and three "letter" or base pairs at a time, a matching tRNA carrying a specific amino acid helps to grow the chain of amino acids. In reality, it isn't so much that the mRNA is fed into the machinery as much as each ribosome rides down the mRNA. We know this because one mRNA can be simultaneously translated by multiple ribosomes at once.

All living things use a similar coding system from this central dogma. As the ribosome advances three mRNA base pairs at a time, a specific amino acid will be added until the stop signal is reached. A decoder chart for matching the universal language of mRNA sequences to their designated amino acids is shown below. Starting with the middle and working outward, the intended amino acid will be added, or the transcription can be started or stopped. There are four types of mRNA molecules which are abbreviated by the letters "GUAC", or guanine, uracil, adenine, and cytosine. If you follow the arrow to just past nine o'clock, you will see that G followed by a C and a U will require either start a new translation or a cause the ribosome to add alanine as the next amino acid for the emerging protein chain.

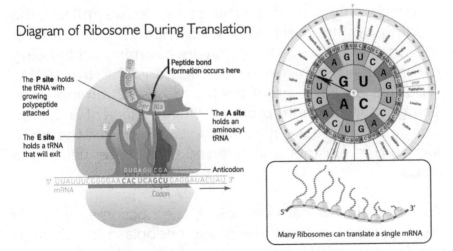

Diagram of Ribosome During Translation

2.2: mRNA to Protein Translation using Ribosomes and tRNA

What makes this dogma so central? Well, in all known forms of life, the process of being alive involves making proteins that are capable of assembly into structures, act as messengers, and regulate complex pathways from immune responses, cell growth and death, and all aspects of homeostasis (staying the same) and metabolism (the economics of energy).

How is this possible? It turns out that those 21 amino acids have certain chemical properties and that when you take a string of them, they will predictably fold in ways that give them repeatable and meaningful shapes based on the ways in which the amino acids attract and repel each other. In fact, there are four levels of complexity when it comes to proteins structure that are shown below.

The primary structure is the precise sequence of amino acids. The secondary structure is the way the local amino acids organize into corkscrews or pleats, for example. The tertiary structure is the way in which regions predictably fold and create shapes. Finally, the quaternary structure is the assembly of discreet proteins into compound structures composed of multiple distinct proteins.

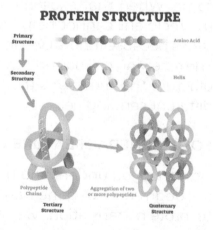

PROTEIN STRUCTURE

Primary Structure — Amino Acid

Secondary Structure — Helix

Polypeptide Chains

Tertiary Structure

Aggregation of two or more polypeptides

Quaternary Structure

2.3: Protein Structure Hierarchy

You may be a bit confused, but in those few paragraphs above, you hopefully have grasped the universal principle of life on planet Earth. There are no known exceptions, from the lowly bacteria to the majestic blue whale or redwood tree. Some of you might be confused because restaurants often ask you whether you want a "protein" to signify meat. In fact, all plants also use the same amino acids as animals, albeit in different ratios. So again, all known life on Earth uses DNA transcription to mRNA "recipes", which are then read by ribosomes to translate them into a primary protein sequence which then forms structures with secondary, tertiary, and sometimes quaternary organization. The appearance, function, and capabilities of all living things are merely emergent properties of how proteins are produced and how their cells organize themselves.

Right about now, you may be asking yourself, "Why should I care about all of this science?" The answer is that if you are a cell and you want to influence another cell, you can just package a protein or, better yet, the recipe for a protein (mRNA) or its specific mRNA blocker and put it into an exosome. When that exosome merges with your target cell, the recipient cannot help but express the intended messages because it now lives in the recipient's cell cytoplasm. The receiving cell has no way of knowing that it didn't manufacture the messages that it has received from a totally different sending cell.

SOME GENERAL FEATURES OF CELL BIOLOGY

Now that you understand the two basic forces of the central dogma – DNA gene transcription to mRNA and mRNA to protein translation, we should introduce a few other concepts that you will need to grasp regarding cell biology. They are gene silencing, stemness, replicative senescence, DNA damage, cell senescence, cell suicide, stem cell depletion, and dedifferentiation.

If proteins are like the notes of the music, then GENE SILENCING serves as the rests between notes or, if you prefer, the notes that are not played because they are "out of key". STEMNESS refers to types of cells responsible for making other cells by acting as templates. REPLICATIVE SENESCENCE is the loss of music from repeatedly copying sheet music. DNA DAMAGE is like the sheet music errors that copying the music or other energetic or chemical accidents can produce. CELL SENESCENCE AND CELL SUICIDE is the like the tendency for musicians to "lose their chops" and be fired or retire. STEM CELL DEPLETION is like the aging out of the teachers and conductors of an orchestra. And finally, DEDIFFERENTIATION is the rebirth of creativity that a composer might enjoy later in life. Let's tackle each of these concepts to build a richer understanding of what is behind the natural progression towards illness and aging.

GENE SILENCING

Gene silencing (and promotion) are the key reasons why cells look and behave differently despite all carrying the same complete genetic blueprints (i.e., the chromosomes and their DNA). Cells with a nucleus can produce every protein because they are all endowed with the complete library. This library is known as the human genome and is usually contained in 23 maternal and 23 paternal chromosomes, which serve as cookbooks with recipes for proteins.

In any actual functioning cell, only a limited number of the proteins are being actively produced because most of the genes are silenced or not expressed. The genetic hardware is the genome, or the 46 chromosomes and their DNA. But EPIGENETIC "software" are the other chemical markings that can also be copied; they determine which proteins that cell will express. These software changes are arguably much more important than the DNA hardware, and some of the epigenetic methods used are the addition of acetyl or methyl groups to the DNA binding proteins, which work like bookmarks. Adding the acetyl group will promote gene transcription by keeping those "pages" opened, whereas adding methyl groups will close those pages like staples.

There are many potential "pages" of the DNA cookbooks to produce all those proteins. The reasons certain cells behave differently are largely due to the proteins that are promoted and suppressed by these epigenetic software changes that are also copied into the two daughter cells when one mother divides into two.

Consider the proteins of cells like various meals a chef might cook. If you add every single known ingredient to every dish, you wouldn't be a very good cook, would you? Likewise, if you tried to add 11,000+ proteins to every single cell you wouldn't have an efficiently functioning, specialized cell. So, depending on what genes are turned on and off, you get different types of cells doing specialized tasks.

Unlike the copying of DNA, which is nearly perfect, there is lower fidelity in the copying of epigenetic software such as acetylation and methylation.[1] The predictable accumulation of more gene silencing has led to interest in the so-called epigenetic "clock" of aging.

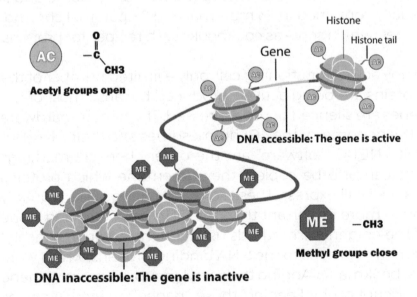

2.4: Epigenetic "Switches"

STEMNESS ·

Fact: nearly every person begins life as a single fertilized egg made from 23 maternal chromosomes and 23 paternal chromosomes. That one egg was the ultimate "stem cell" with the potential to make all your roughly 37 trillion cells and express the recipes for 11,000+ proteins. But what exactly defines a "stem cell"? Well, there are generally two agreed-upon features: relative immortality by lengthening the telomeres at the ends of the chromosomes and the capacity for asymmetric division. **Telomerase activation** is something you can learn about in my first two non-fiction books, *Telomere Timebombs*, and *The Telomere Miracle*.

Asymmetric division means that a mother divides into a more specialized or differentiated daughter and a stem-like mother with the ability to stay immortal and less differentiated.

Asymmetric Division in Stem Cells

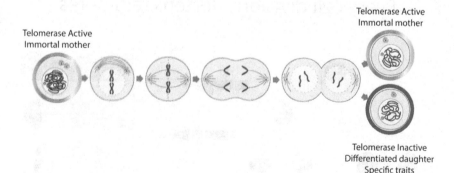

2.5: Asymmetric Division Defines "Stemness"

So, how does this daughter versus mother differentiation take place? We don't really know yet, but there are likely both physical and software (epigenetic) mechanisms involved.

REPLICATIVE SENESCENCE

I spend a fair amount of time at anti-aging conferences listening to experts. One thing that is often ignored because it doesn't fit their paradigm is replicative senescence. I hear people talk about the pineal gland, DNA methylation as a so-called biological "clock," and other theories of hormonal decline. What they fail to mention is that all the above processes can be attributable to depletion of stem cells via replicative senescence.

What is this thing called replicative senescence? Without going into excessive detail, just understand that when a cell divides, the protective ends or telomeres, must shorten 50 to 100 base pair units. There are no exceptions to this rule, and that means that a non-stem cell differentiated cell lineage can only copy 50 to 70 times before it is no longer viable. That limitation has been referred to as the Hayflick limit.

Every cell division shortens telomeres

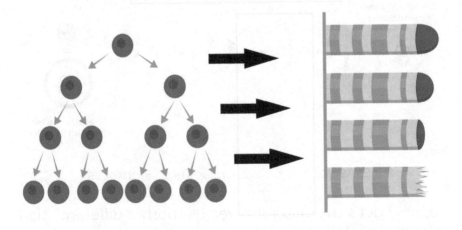

Cells Divide   Telomeres Shorten

2.6: Replicative Senescence

In contrast, recall that stem cells can be relatively immortal by lengthening their telomeres in between cell divisions. This process is not 100% effective, and if telomeres become absent, the DNA protection machinery misinterprets uncapped (telomere absent) ends as ripped-apart chromosomes and performs end-to-end fusion, which is an artificial splicing together like trapeze artists glued at their hands. The problem with that is when the chromosomes separate during the next cell division, the trapeze artists are torn apart, causing not only an abnormal chromosome number (**aneuploidy**, pronounced AN-yuh-ploydee) in both daughters but also breaks in the DNA leading to gene mutations.

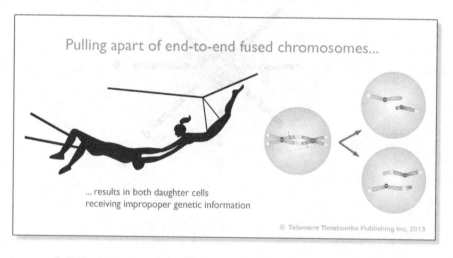

Pulling apart of end-to-end fused chromosomes...

... results in both daughter cells
receiving impropoper genetic information

© Telomere Timebombs Publishing Inc, 2013

2.7: Trapeze artists illustrate chromosome damage

In the case of damage, as would occur with overused joints, the rapid copying of local stem cells causes their telomeres to shorten with each cell division. Suppose they don't have adequate time to recover the length with telomerase. In that case, those stem cells "age" and eventually become dysfunctional or suicidal due to failure of an internal chromosomal number checkpoint that takes place before cell division.

So, the inadequate lengthening of stem cell telomeres is a necessary and sufficient condition for dysfunction and depletion of stem cells and can account for the processes of disease and aging that we recognize on a larger scale. Here is a diagram from my first book that shows the central role of telomere shortening, which has been correlated with nearly every known disease and is, I believe, one of the primary reasons why we get sick and die.

Short telomeres play a central role in the development of age-related diseases

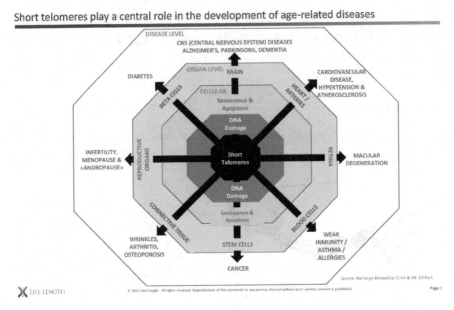

2.8: Octagon of aging and illness

Replicative senescence causes weakened immunity, poor circulation, inadequate organ function, and is the driving force behind human disease and aging.

DNA DAMAGE

I once attended a lecture by a health influencer/guru who said, "I am not a doctor, I am not a scientist, but I know your DNA remains the same throughout your life." Well, as the rock star Meatloaf sang, "Two out of three ain't bad." In fact, your DNA does change throughout life. There is replicative senescence causing stem cell mutation and depletion. Also, the copying of DNA is not error-free and with time, we become error-ridden and genetically mutated strangers unto ourselves.

CELL SENESCENCE AND SUICIDE

Cell senescence is a vague term, but let's try to unpack it. How do you know a person is old? If a frozen embryo is incubated after thirty years, is it born thirty years and ten months old? Yes and no. For all intents and purposes, the baby looks and acts like a newborn. If a child with premature accelerated aging from telomerase dysfunction (Dyskeratosis congenita) has been alive for only ten years, are her cells ten years old? Yes and no. For all intents and purposes, her cells and biology resemble that of an octogenarian.[2]

Interestingly, there are several pathways to getting old at an accelerated rate. When we study these premature aging syndromes, the classic ones result in hair loss, greying, and diseases of old age, and they all involve DNA replication problems or structural instability of the genome, like failure to maintain telomeres.

Recently, the use of epigenetic markers to assess cell aging has been validated and adopted extensively. Unfortunately, although the correlation between one's chronological age and epigenetic silencing patterns is very high, the specific reasons behind this correlation don't yet make up a coherent theory of causation. It is just data mining for specific notes in a concert score, but the music theory isn't understood yet.

Returning to the notion of how we know a cell is old, there are several ways we can conceptualize the problem. Some have described the **senescence-associated secretory phe-notype (SASP)** as one of the hallmarks of cell aging. We could think of it as like the "old people smell" that you may remember from childhood. There is inflammation, and that causes certain strange proteins to be produced. What is an old anything? It is slow, cranky, unable to function, has difficulty procreating, loses its energy, and becomes with-ered in appearance.

What is interesting is that when we have damage, we bring inflammation but also induce stem cell replication. If you surgically damage a young mouse's knees, the carti-lage stem cells will copy so fast that they become "old" by standard measures. However the addition of MSCs or their exosomes could partially alleviate this aging and acceler-ate recovery.[3]

There are various ways in which cells are killed by our own immune systems, but in the main, they are programmed to kill themselves. I reached this epiphany when I began to understand cancer as a problem of cell suicide dysfunc-tion. The use of protein tests to detect preclinical cancer is problematic because when you do prophylactic surgery, often the pathologists cannot find the trouble-making cells if they even still exist. If the cancer cells are too few to be a tumor and if they were destined to self-destruct or be cleared, this "overtreatment" is a risk of early detection.

Basically, cancer is usually engendered by the loss of certain regulatory genes, most probably in the already immortal stem cells. Although some argue that dedifferentiation of cells is often at work, it can likely occur either way. In other words, a stem cell can become mutated, or a daughter cell can become a more primitive mother stem cell. The truth is that we probably get potential cancer many times, but they never come to fruition because of cell suicide and immune surveillance. Once a cancer becomes clinically apparent, the best way to remediate is often surgery, then radiation locally, then chemotherapy. That is because each of the cancer treatments is increasingly damaging to normal healthy stem cells, especially in the crucial immune cells and vascularity. Here is a pyramid that I thought of from my first non-fiction book: *Telomere Timebombs*

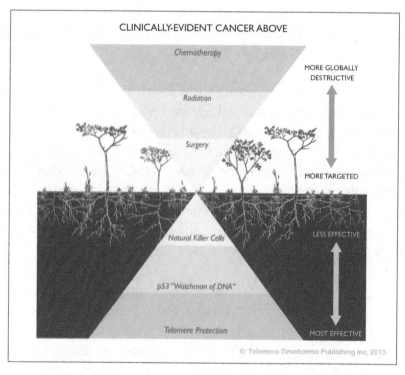

CLINICALLY-EVIDENT CANCER ABOVE

Chemotherapy

MORE GLOBALLY
DESTRUCTIVE

Radiation

Surgery

MORE TARGETED

Natural Killer Cells

LESS EFFECTIVE

p53 "Watchman of DNA"

Telomere Protection

MOST EFFECTIVE

© Telomere Timebombs Publishing Inc, 2013

2.9: Prevention and Treatment of Cancer

In any case, cancer is primarily a genetic problem and is, as my pyramid suggests, usually handled by cell suicide. One of the main mechanisms of that suicide is the p53 protein, called "the watchman" of the genome. When the chromosome number is incorrect, as happens when the telomeres shorten and then the trapeze artists separate unequally, something called the **DNA damage checkpoint activation** is triggered and the p53 orchestrates the mitochondria to have holes which leak out the battery acid inside and cause the cell to die like the Wicked Witch of the West having water poured on her.

STEM CELL DEPLETION

Scientists often study the elderly because they hope to find clues, but in truth, they were just the last to survive the game of musical chairs that is stem cell depletion. Science would do better to find ways to keep the music going and stop removing chairs if they want to increase human lifespan.

In 2014, scientists analyzed the blood of a Dutch lady, 115-yo Hendrikje van Andel-Schipper, then the oldest woman in the world. They found that all her white blood cells, the ones that fight infection and recognize damaged cells, were descended from only two **HSCs (hematopoietic stem cells)** with shortened telomeres, instead of the usual 11,000 in a young person.[4] Through the process of being just being alive, she had acquired at least 450 mutations during her lifetime in one of two cell lines.[5]

What does this mean? Because a healthy, young immune system is like a locksmith with many blank keys, the continuous use of blank keys over a lifetime depletes them. No complex epigenetic theory of aging is required if we only consider that stem cell copying itself can cause DNA mutation. Inadequate telomerase extension of the stem cell telomeres causes replicative senescence and DNA/gene mutation. Consider that all throughout your body you have stem cell mothers that are also acquiring errors, getting shorter telomeres, and undergoing automatic suicide. Now you have a notion of why there is depletion in "Everything, everywhere, all at once".

What can we do to remediate this? Well, when you are twenty-years old, you can store mesenchymal, **hematopoietic** (blood producing), and **epithelial** (vessel producing) stem cells for future use. This should probably be a human right for everyone because, unlike the non-scientist, non-doctor, guru's claim, your DNA is NOT the same throughout your life. You are constantly mutating and diverging into a genetically chimeric stranger unto yourself. This genetic divergence is also likely a driver of aging.

At this moment, there are thousands of scientists around the world with the knowledge of how to cause stem cells to differentiate into specific cell types by introducing certain biochemical signals because they do it all the time. Prompting stem cells to differentiate into bone, fat, or cartilage cells is a fundamental heuristic (practical test) of how you know the cells are actually mesenchymal stem cells. If you read a paper and did some training, you could be one of them. What is not known, but what soon may be, is how to create ANY kind of stem cell using stem cell relatives and tuning them with specific signals. Interestingly, stem cell scientists actually use the musical term "tuning" to describe their manipulation of stem cell differentiation.

So why would you want to store your own stem cells? Because despite being a "close match" even identical twins become genetically divergent over a lifetime. Because taking someone else's stem cells is an automatic immune challenge, those stem cells live only for days in most cases. Studies from mice indicate that MSCs from an unmatched donor primarily get trapped in the lungs, don't migrate to sites of injury, and are gone within 24 hours.[6] The reason they are beneficial in some cases is not engraftment but rather that they do secrete exosomes before they are killed.

But let's just say for the sake of argument that they could engraft and survive in you despite being mismatched in terms of histocompatibility complex proteins (the self-identity we will explain later). We now have a problem of genetically unmatched daughter cells, which at best, would result in genetic confusion, but at worst, could lead to autoimmune problems.

Why not use embryonic stem cells? That is actually a very important thought experiment which brings us back to the concept of cell differentiation. Remember when we said you as a fertilized egg were destined to become 37 trillion cells and walk around the Earth? As a zygote, you were OMNI (all) potent or powerful. As you grow in the womb, there are epigenetic switches that get triggered leading to loss of potentiality, and those switches are, thankfully, hard to remove. In cases where scientists did try using early embryonic stem cells for their tremendous potentiality, **teratomas** (or monster tumors) could sometimes grow because the ability to become many things was not yet switched off. A teratoma contains endoderm, mesoderm, ectoderm and in practical terms might look like a greasy mass of teeth, nerves, and fat. Teratomas can come from embryonic stem cells that have too little differentiation and too much potentiality.

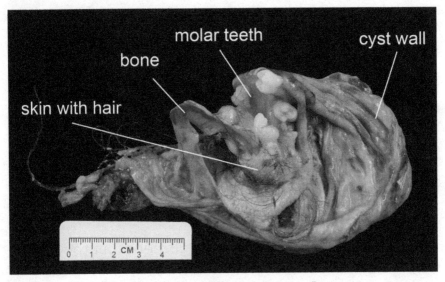

2.10: Teratoma of the Ovary[7]

So, if you had stored your stem cells at age 20, what advantage do you have? Well, most people will have to spend a lot of money getting a genetically incompatible stranger's stem cells, or they can try replacing their own damaged stem cells with more of the damaged stem cells. The person who banked when they were young has original equipment manufacturer (OEM) stem cells that they can use to restore a 20-year-old version of their cell functioning. And because you don't thaw them all at once and they can be expanded in numbers after that future thaw date, the supply of youthful cells is nearly infinite, and their uses will be limited only by scientific knowledge on how to direct their differentiation to needed cell types.

So, what do you do if you never banked your own stem cells? Actually, there was a trend to save umbilical cord blood in the late 20th century until now so there is a chance you do have usable stem cells frozen somewhere if your parents kept up with the storage payments. There are ample HSCs and MSCs from cord blood, so you are in luck![8] Although from a newborn placenta, they are still considered "adult" stem cells because they no longer have the embryonic potentiality and risks of teratoma formation.

The laws surrounding stem cell autograft (giving to yourself) are in evolution as the FDA maintained that a person couldn't harvest, freeze, store, thaw, and multiply their own stem cells without bringing unacceptable risk into the process. That is why people travel elsewhere. In a case of the USA versus California Stem Cell Treatment Center, Inc. et al., the FDA lost, but the case is currently in appeal.[9] The implications for your ability to make replacement parts for yourself from your banked stem cells are significant.

DEDIFFERENTIATION

If you understand that we all began as an omnipotent single cell (a fertilized egg) and ended up with many different types of specialized stem cells and their differentiated daughters, then you realize there is power in being able to go backwards in terms of differentiation.

Consider the poster species for regeneration: the axolotl salamander. It can regenerate limbs, presumably by virtue of its ability to revisit the embryonic behaviors and cell types that generated them originally. While this ability would be great for us in case of a human amputation, in most cases, we do not want to have the ability to grow extra limbs by triggering that degree of dedifferentiation.

There are at least two basic ways to cause dedifferentiation. Firstly, there are some **microRNA (aka miRNA)** sequences that block specific messenger RNA sequences and some **small interfering (aka siRNA)** double-stranded RNA that can accomplish this. Cells can tonically, or constantly, express repressors of primitive dedifferentiation. The blocking of those messenger RNAs with a specific microRNA or siRNA is one way in which cells can de-differentiate and become more primitive.[10]

The second way of inducing pluripotency is with the Yamanaka factors. Four genes and their proteins were found in 2006 to potentially cause differentiated daughters to become pluripotent mothers. Those genes were Oct4, Sox2, Klf4, and cMyc, and this discovery was awarded a Nobel Prize in 2012. There have since been other factors identified.

Although there are likely other unknown ways in which cells can become de-differentiated, scientists are still far from being able to master the dance of differentiation. Perhaps someday, they will be able to take any stored stem cell and reengineer replacement parts for everyone using a deeper understanding of cell music theory and tuning.

I don't want to leave you with the impression that dedifferentiation is something only for salamanders or extreme cases of genetic manipulation because the truth is that dedifferentiation is probably happening for different reasons as a part of everyday life and that we just don't understand how to harness it yet.

GENE THERAPY

The ability to introduce wanted genes (DNA segments that code for specific proteins) using viral vectors is well known. Perhaps there is some use for this when we consider that elephants, who rarely get cancer, have twenty copies of the p53 gene (remember the cell suicide watchman of the genome?).[11] The problem with gene therapy is that it randomly inserts the genes anywhere into the DNA, and that can, itself, cause mutations. The same problem holds true for gene editing with CRISPR-Cas9. Random placement is an issue for unpredictable genetic damage, so in general, it would be preferable to use the existing normal cells to remediate problems of aging and disease.

Important exceptions to this might be in the case of genetic inborn mutations of critical genes that produce known specific diseases. In those cases, having active copies of the missing essential proteins might justify the risk of intentionally changing the host DNA.

In conclusion, this chapter was a crash course in cell biology. We learned about the central dogma of how the genome encodes the proteins. We learned that all cells come from one cell, and their behavior is a function of which genes are expressed through epigenetic switches. Stem cells can be primitive and possess a lot of potential when we are embryos, but after birth, they become many types of cells, yet they tend to specialize and create specific cell types that suit specific organs and purposes. Throughout life, the shortening of telomeres causes aging of those stem cells, which produces mutation and loss of their original functioning as well as depletion from cell suicide.

In the grand scheme of things, we are made up of cells. These cells have their own lineages, hardware, software, environments, music for communication, and destinies. But the overall process, if left to its own devices, results in losses of viable stem cells, losses of genetic integrity, and losses of functional reserve. These are the general trends in a human life progressing towards illness and aging, but now that we understand them, we are closer to mitigating those challenges.

Chapter 3

MY JOURNEY

Some people feel the rain. Others just get wet.

—Bob Dylan

In the first chapter, we explained that all living cells make exosomes to influence each other and that this is a new paradigm. The second chapter explained some fundamentals of cell biology that pertain to why we age and become less functional. In this third chapter, I will try to introduce myself to you.

There are many ways, from the demographic to the metaphysical, to explain a person. As I write this, I am a 56-year-old Korean-American divorced father of two grown sons working as a medical doctor in regenerative medicine and based out of Southern California. I am licensed in four other states: Texas, Florida, Hawaii, and New York, and I travel regularly to treat patients in those states as well.

I am also an invited speaker who lectures on the clinical use of exosomes to other doctors. As an educator, I created a twelve-hour online provider training course for those who wish to understand and implement this new and powerful modality in their clinical practices.

But how did I get here? For that explanation, we need to start a little earlier.

My father was born during the Japanese colonization of Korea in 1932. From 1910 to 1945, an attempt was made to replace the language and culture of Korea and make it a Japanese vassal state. As such, Dad's primary language was Japanese, and for the rest of his life, he would refer to the Japanese-English dictionary even though he was completely fluent in Korean and English.

Because of the devastations of Japanese colonization and two wars, my father's family didn't have the resources to send him to high school. Luckily, the Confucian meritocracy system in East Asia allowed him to study at home, and his determination and hard work paid off; through high stakes blinded exams, he earned admission to the top two universities in Korea. He went on to study medicine and then after compulsory military service, he travelled to the USA to do a series of different residencies until his visa expired and he and my mom, a nursing exchange student, had to emigrate to Canada with their firstborn, my sister. From my father, I learned a love for learning and from my mother, I learned that with determination, anything was possible.

I was born in the summer of 1967, two years after my middle brother, as the third child of Korean twice immigrated parents in the capital of Saskatchewan, Regina. In 1970, at the age of three, I emigrated with my family to Southern California into the Jewish neighborhood of Crenshaw two months before the Sylmar earthquake. I still recall falling out of the lower bunk of our bed and completing my slumber on the floor. Soon after, our family moved to the San Gabriel Valley further east, where I would grow up until leaving for college. My mother was a stereotypical Asian "tiger mom" and sought out the best educational opportunities, leading my sister, then my brother, and then myself in fifth grade to a small preparatory school in South Pasadena called The Polytechnic School.

Thanks to genetics, great teachers, and inspiring peers, the new school wasn't too difficult, and I managed to learn what I needed to grow as a person and prepare for college. Like my sister and brother before me, I attended Harvard College, where I majored in anthropology with a premed focus. Immediately after college, I attended New York's Columbia University, where I earned a Master of Public Health degree along with my Doctor of Medicine.

Without interruption, I then matched to Boston's Beth Israel Hospital, which is a Harvard University teaching hospital. Those four years gave me a wealth of clinical experience as we rotated through medical, surgical, and Ob-Gyn specialties. After residency, I moved with my wife to Orange County, California, to work for four years in the Kaiser Permanente system, which was also a very challenging clinical experience that helped me become a better doctor. During that time, I became board-certified as well.

In 2001, I decided to establish my own private practice in Orange County. Almost half of my patients were Spanish-speaking, which was fine because I was fluent. I also had a fair number of Korean patients as I was conversant in the language. The practice of Ob-Gyn was stressful, yet it suited me because of the many opportunities to help and because it rarely resulted in sad outcomes.

I had always imagined myself working in a public health service role, like Doctors Without Borders, but the exigencies of raising two small children led me to continue practicing in the United States. I expanded my practice to include cosmetic lasers, botox, and injectable fillers. Things seemed to be going well until 2010, when an investigation into using Mexican IUDs led me to lose my ability to practice clinical ob-gyn for some years.

My mentor at Columbia, who was also the dean of the School of Public Health, was Allen Rosenfield, the son of the former chairman of Beth Israel's Ob-Gyn department, as fate would have it. Under him, I learned of the Copper-T IUD, developed by Rosenfield's own Population Council and gifted to countries like India and Mexico. Ironically, I had lectured on behalf of the USAID in El Salvador regarding this IUD as part of a job interview for a public health position with a group called Family Health International, who later offered me a job supervising contraception in Mongolia.

When the most prominent Latin-American ob-gyns in my area told me everyone was using the more affordable Mexican versions, I just assumed wrongly that would be okay. Given what I knew about the history and safety of the Copper-T, it seemed okay, but in the eyes of our drug manufacturers and regulatory agencies, the use of less than twenty IUDs imported from Mexico (but not Canada) warranted a loss in my ability to bill Medicaid.

Although the government said I was still competent to see patients, I could not bill for them. But, since this had repercussions for hospital privileges, I felt compelled to resign from all my hospital appointments. So essentially, my clinical ob-gyn practice was effectively over, although I never received any sanctions against my practice of medicine, and the misdemeanor conviction was reversed after community service.

Luckily, I had been taking and selling TA-65, a small molecule telomerase activator, for three years, and my income from that was even better than being a practicing doctor. I also had an unusually lucky streak in the stock market. So, I decided to create more content about aging and telomeres, which to date, has resulted in more than a million views on YouTube.

Since 2009, I have been in the anti-aging space, giving many lectures about my stem cell theory of aging. Because of my videos, lectures, and blogging, I became an opinion leader in the anti-aging world. By attending anti-aging conferences with the same anti-aging gurus for over fourteen years, I have concluded that their ideas don't always translate into visible results. When I started taking a telomerase activator in 2007, I was 25 lbs heavier, had grey hair, and was using reading glasses at the age of 40.

Now, at 56, I see the gurus I've known for years, and they all look like they are aging normally, if not at an accelerated pace. Admittedly, this is an anecdotal observation. However, for the last sixteen years, I've not had a recurrence of my fatty liver, hypertension, grey hair, and presbyopia (reading glasses) despite only taking that one supplement and no hormones. In fact, knock on wood, I am the only person in their 50s whom I can recall has never had surgery, has all 32 teeth, doesn't take prescription medicines, and is pain-free throughout their body. Before you attribute this to lifestyle, ask the donut shop and the convenience store clerks across the street the kinds of things that I typically buy.

So, I know and reunite with these health gurus, but they don't get carded for alcohol on a regular basis like yours truly. So what? So, telomerase activation works, according to the people checking identification for purchasing adult beverages. Here is an unretouched mashup of myself, my two sons, and my mom through the years.

22 YRS OF AGING ON TELOMERASE ACTIVATORS!

Scan QR for my contact info and to download all my Exosome Educational Information

2022 (Ages 23 & 85)

2000 (Ages 1 & 33) 2010 (Ages 43 & 10) 2016 (Ages 13, 17 & 49) 2022 (Ages 19, 23 & 55)

3.1: Twenty-two years of aging while on Telomerase Activators

Through my experiences of providing telomerase activators to patients, I learned a great deal about human health, disease, and physiology. This whole phase was prompted by my father's battle with brain cancer. For the first time, in my late 30s, I wondered why people got old, and my intuition and reasoning led me to create a stem cell theory of aging. That theory became the basis for a sci-fi graphic novel, and two non-fiction books, *Telomere Timebombs*, and *The Telomere Miracle*.

At the end of 2014, a person who had been following my videos and blogs contacted me and asked me to give him a ride to see the premiere of a movie called *The Immortalists*. For the next three years, I worked to consult for him on anti-aging generally in many emails, calls, and monthly meetings. I made recommendations on which companies had promising technologies, and although it was an unpaid position, I learned about exosomes from a physician that I recruited to join us. This collaboration resulted in the launch of a successful company for that physician who is still selling a freeze-dried exosome product for skin care.

Shortly thereafter, in December of 2018, I was attending the American Academy of Anti-Aging Medicine conference in Las Vegas, when I heard a lecture on exosomes. The science was already something familiar to me, but the personal story by a physician of his motorcycle accident four weeks prior intrigued me. In the past, I had had a bruised intercostal muscle from snowboarding and that made it difficult to speak and laugh for weeks. This man in his mid-60s claimed to have fallen from a motorcycle and broken his collar bone, multiple ribs, and his ankle. According to his account, he administered five vials of exosomes into his own vein, and despite the horrific accident in which he had lost a third of his blood, he was now speaking in front of a large audience, without difficulty, just four weeks after the event. He also stated that there was no x-ray evidence of ever having had a fracture in his ankle.

At this point, the mind reels and quickly gravitates to two possibilities: massive confabulation or some unusual healing potential. Through a bit of serendipity, I was invited to attend dinner with the CEO and lead scientist of the only exosome manufacturer at the time, and the impression that I got was that they were manufacturing the exosomes from mesenchymal stem cells with a high degree of quality control, reproducibility, and analytic rigor.

So, in early 2019, I decided to put the exosomes to the test and purchased some to experiment on myself. Years earlier, from a nearly maniacal repeated golf swing session, I had torn a right knee meniscus. From yoga, I had also a strained rotator cuff and Achilles' tendon. To my surprise and delight, all three conditions improved to the point of not hurting. In the last four years, I have had to reinject the rotator cuff and Achilles' twice each, but the clicking and pain in the knee has never recurred.

I then attempted to test the safety and efficacy of a technique I had learned during my stem cell clinical training: nasal injection. To my surprise, a nasal injection dose caused two interesting phenomena. After one hour, I felt excited, like the sensation of being nearly at the apex of a tall roller coaster. After two hours, I acquired (or unlocked) an unusual ability that very few people have: voluntary piloerection. Despite not repeating the nasal injection, four years later, I can still cause all the hairs on my body to make goosebumps simply by thinking about it.

It seemed that the basic science of mesenchymal stem cells (which we explore later), my years of studying exosomes, hearing of that doctor's accident, and the dinner with the exosome company's founder had led me to something that was able to positively impact my own acquired damage but also unlocked that strange new capability.

Before embarking on an expansion of my practice, I decided to try it on a limited number of close patients and my mom. My siblings were, and continue to be, non-believers, but my 86-yo mother has received over thirty-three treatments to date, and she loves it. Wherever she has pain, be it in her arthritic knuckles, her back, hips, shoulders, knees, ankles, and elsewhere, we inject exosomes and the pains disappear.

Although I was facile with ultrasound from being an Ob-Gyn, I chose to attend a seminar on ultrasound-guided joint injections and acquired malpractice insurance to begin my practice. Gradually, over the last four years, I have treated hundreds of patients, most of whom choose to repeat therapy, in over 1800 injections. As a result, I have created many blogs, lectures, webinars, and even an online 12-hour training course for providers. To access those educational materials, find my profile at www.ovou.me/edwardpark or go to www.rechargebiomedical.com

As we will discuss in the following chapter on mesenchymal stem cells (MSC), the general results of injecting MSC exosomes are predictable, related to dose, accretive in benefits, anti-inflammatory, and stimulate regeneration in many cases.

At this moment, there aren't any books that attempt to explain to a lay audience this important new development in regenerative medicine. So, I decided to self-publish this book to share what I've learned.

They say that a life is comprised of what happens to you but more importantly, how you respond to those challenges. I have no bitterness for temporarily losing my ability to practice Ob-Gyn because it led me to learn more about regenerative medicine, and as a result, I've been able to help a greater number of people with techniques that didn't previously exist. My hope with this book is that people, both patients and providers, will open their minds to the existence of biohacking with exosomes for the purpose of mitigating aging and disease.

Metaphysically, some believe that ancestors and spirits actively conspire to help us and guide us. I don't know if that is literally true, but I certainly do see a pattern. I have always wanted to make the world a better place, first with public health, then screenwriting, and by teaching patients and providers about telomeres and now exosomes. If what I believe about exosomes and their potential is true, this may be the most important contribution that I could make to date.

Chapter 4

THE MESENCHYMAL STEM CELL (MSC)

Establish enigmas, not explanations.

—Robert Smithson (artist)

We discuss MSC stem cells and their exosomes for two reasons. Firstly, they are likely the primary mediators of healing throughout your body for your entire life. Secondly, our clinical experience in using them indicates that we can use these types of exosomes to mitigate illness and facilitate wellness.

Okay, it's cards on the table time. I am not an expert in stem cells. But then again, no one else is either. Because the most specialized and knowledgeable scientist is equally unable to interpret the music and dances of cell biology, we are all quite ignorant about matters as important as cell differentiation, de-differentiation, and communication. Thankfully, if you have understood what you have read thus far, we can at least speculate about things that will lessen our shared ignorance.

Let's start with a few safe assumptions about the world of cells generally and of stem cells specifically. You and I developed from one omnipotent stem cell, the fertilized egg, but now consist of many organs working together. Those organs are comprised of rare, specialized stem cells in local **niches** and many terminally differentiated daughter cells. We call them terminally differentiated because they tend not to de-differentiate, they are highly specialized, and they have lifespans due to their inability to lengthen their telomeres (Hayflick limited). Stem cells are somewhat differentiated and specialized by epigenetic software. They look and act differently depending on whether you find them in the brain, the retinas, the kidneys, bones, muscles, etc.

The ability of local stem cells in those organs to replenish our normal functioning is a negotiation between what is needed and what is available. As we age, stem cell DNA can mutate and the epigenetic switches determining gene expression can change; these changes result in diminishing or abnormal function and cell death.

The take-home point is that every cell has its own ancestry. Through the process of differentiation, which is largely a function of epigenetic software changes that are inherited from ancestors, every cell is most closely related to its most recent ancestor and then to its local mother stem cell in that organ's niche (i.e., the local environment in the cartilage, kidney, or brain, for example.)

For us non-salamander animals, it is important to grasp that different rules apply to life early in the womb, versus outside the womb. Although the induction of Yamanaka factors to induce pluripotency in normal differentiated daughter cells is an exciting clue, it by no means signifies that we have a useful understanding of how and why cells are more pluripotent rather than differentiated. Moreover, the induction of primitive embryonic-like cells is a dangerous game that mother nature herself rarely plays because of risks of teratomas, cancers, and untoward effects. That is why I am skeptical that the clinical use of induced pluripotency will be a usable technology for improving human health.

Let us first explore some of the important features of **embryogenesis** (the development of an embryo) so that we can further grasp some of the terminology used when discussing mesenchymal stem cells.

Very early in embryogenesis, the ball of cells called the blastula, which develops into an invaginated structure known as the gastrula and this structure has three layers: the ectoderm, mesoderm, and endoderm.

HUMAN EMBRYONIC DEVELOPMENT

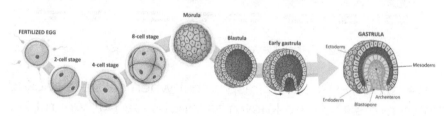

4.1: Embryogenesis

In the subsequent creation of the organs, these three germ layers tend to create different cell types, again by virtue of unknown epigenetic "switches" that turn them into committed, more specific types of less potent, but still pluri-(many) potent stem cells. The more specific the role in the organ, the more committed and inflexible that cell's programming will be. Here are some of the common destinies of those three layers:

The problem with understanding the naming of the mesenchymal stem cell is that it isn't a specific thing but rather a way of being stem-like. They were named that because they resembled stem cells that emerge early in embryogenesis from the primitive connective tissue of the middle mesodermal layer known as the mesenchyme.

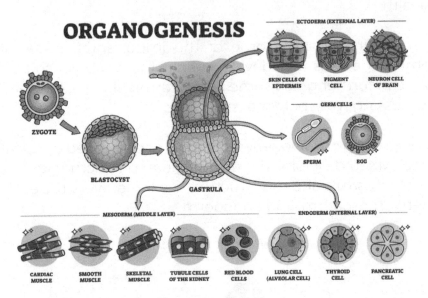

4.2: Germ Layers and Organogenesis

One thing we need to grasp is that when cells are packed into sheets, they are known as "epithelial" but when they act like traveling amoebas, they are known as mesenchymal. Organs can be comprised of cells from all three germ lines, bringing even more confusion into the picture.

There is an important phenomenon that hints at the plasticity of stem cell behavior, and it is known as the mesenchymal-epithelial transition or its inverse, the epithelial-mesenchymal transition. Early in embryogenesis, sheets of cells can arise from the free amoeboid mesenchymal stem cells via this mesenchymal-epithelial transition. Inversely, the mesenchymal cells can arise from epithelial cells throughout our lives.[1]

One of the pioneering scientists who named the mesenchymal stem cell was Dr. Arnold Caplan. He has spent a lifetime concluding that throughout our adult lives, not just embryonic life, the MSCs are derived from pericytes. **Pericytes** are amoeboid cells that line most of the small blood vessels or capillaries throughout our bodies, but they can undergo an epithelial-mesenchymal transition.

One of the defining traits of MSCs, other than their ability to move and their lack of cell adhesion and polarity, is their ability to transform into different types of cells. This is known as the "**mesengenic**" process, and it is the primary heuristic for MSC validation.[2]

Every stem cell biologist I've ever met was very proud of the fact that they have learned the alchemy of testing to see if the cell you have in culture is an actual MSC. By adding certain signaling molecules to the cell culture, they can reliably induce the multipotent cells to "become", in form and appearance, specific differentiated cells such as bone, cartilage, muscle, tendons etc.

If a pluripotent MSC can be made to undergo mesengenic differentiation in a dish, wouldn't mother nature be able to accomplish the same in vivo? What this means is that throughout our body, we have cells that can, under the right conditions, probably create new tissues themselves and they are living right there in blood vessels feeding those organs.

That makes the initial assumption that we don't regenerate adult organs in a manner similar to in utero conditions somewhat debatable. The implications that tissue and organ regeneration might involve controlled embryonic-like behaviors, at least by virtue of the MSC's mesengenic capacity, are exciting. The larger implications are that we may someday learn how to deftly manipulate the "music" of cell differentiation choices, not only in the multi-purpose

MSCs that generate our musculoskeletal system above but also in the more fragile and complex organs like the brain and kidney.

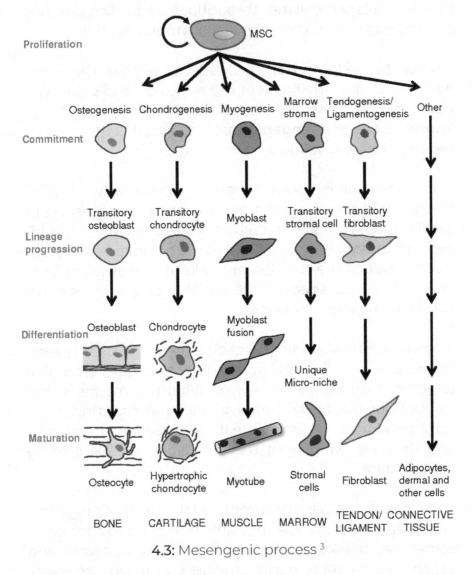

4.3: Mesengenic process [3]

MSC: TIME FOR A NAME CHANGE?

Dr. Arnold Caplan has spent the recent years of his life trying to rename his own discovery. He argues in "Mesenchymal Stem Cells: Time to Change the Name!" that they should rather be called "medicinal signaling cells" instead.[4] The reasons for this are complex and nuanced, but to sum them up, he has concluded that these ubiquitous cells in the body are not, as with the scientist testing mesengenic potential in a dish, differentiating into specific cell types and engrafting into the needed end organ tissue. I know I just suggested otherwise, but Caplan insists that their primary mode of action is via "medicinal signaling". Plainly speaking, he believes that yes, they can migrate to the sites of damage, but that their primary roles are to conduct immunomodulation (to decrease inflammation primarily) and to orchestrate trophic (growth) efforts by using exosomes to signal the local niche stem cells into copying.

When you get injured, your MSC stem cells are attracted to, or just leave the local capillaries, to release many exosomes. These exosomes act on the immune cells that have also been attracted to the area and cause them to be less inflammatory. Again, the MSC exosomes cause the local stem cells of the damaged area to regenerate by cell division and perhaps cause some de-differentiation of those stem cells as well.

Unlike the axolotl salamander, which can easily mimic in-utero conditions that cause the initial limbs to grow, we appear to have a compromise. For a brief and controlled time, we can potentially cause abnormal healing in a damaged system with these MSC exosomes. Sure, the rapid copying of something like cartilage-producing chondrocyte stem cells can cause premature aging and senescence, but nevertheless, the MSCs and their exosomes are specifically designed and able to conduct regeneration. From birth until death, that is how they function naturally throughout your body.

Unless you are someone who easily incorporates new information, this chapter was perhaps a bit confusing, but there are only really two take-home points. Firstly, MSCs are cells that exist everywhere in the body to conduct repair and regeneration, <u>primarily</u> by releasing their exosomes to make the immune system and local stem cells act differently. Secondly, none of us are really very clear on how stem cell ecology works but as the years progress, more of the music theory will be revealed.

Chapter 5

A BRIEF HISTORY OF REGENERATIVE MEDICINE

Out of clutter, find simplicity.

—Albert Einstein

In the first paragraph of this book, I told you something important, and now I will repeat it. You can do all the internet research and ask any expert that you want, and these things will remain true: MSCs exist as pericytes lining your capillaries, and when you are injured or require repair, they release exosomes to provoke repair and regeneration. You are a machine, but unlike a car, you are somewhat able to repair yourself using MSC exosomes that activate local stem cell niches.

There are a lot of experts who come up with theories about one protein, one signaling pathway, a fad diet, or some magical nutrient that they believe is a "game changer." I did the same thing when I told you about the telomerase-activating astragalus extract that I've taken for the last sixteen years. But inside your own exosomes from MSCs are dozens of proteins, mRNAs, and miRNAs that have been evolutionarily determined to help repair. You could follow experts down their profit and prestige rabbit holes, or you can just assume that Mother Nature has her own expertise in regenerative medicine.

What is in these exosomes? Well, researchers and manufacturers have some general ideas of the notes, melodies, and harmonies because after isolation, they can analyze the contents. After size exclusion filtration of the stem cell media, they can painstakingly use a detergent like Triton X-100 to dissolve the phospholipid bilayers and then identify and quantify the contents using standardized assays for the known proteins and mRNAs. Why do they do this? If you have ever seen the vending machines in supermarkets aimed at kids, they have plastic bubbles with toys or stickers inside them. Unless you crack open the plastic bubbles, you don't have any toys, do you? By the same reasoning, if you send a vial of frozen exosomes to a lab and ask them to analyze them without telling them they need to use detergent to melt the exosome phospholipid walls, then the analysis will come back as nothing but normal saline! Interestingly, a competitor to the company that I use for my exosomes did exactly that, prompting me to blog about the misconception that the vials we use contain only normal saline. [1]

Again, you ask: "So what is inside these exosomes?" I could list proteins and the messenger RNAs, as well as the microRNA that block specific messenger RNAs, but in general, you wouldn't find this very helpful unless you are a molecular biologist. At the end of the chapter, I will list some of the commonly identified proteins and mRNAs for those who might be interested.

Suffice it to say that many of the contents do some predictably desirable and interesting tasks when considering recovery from injury. The first is that they contain immune modulating signals that shift the white blood cells into acting less inflammatory and more towards regeneration. Secondly, there are growth factors that promote cell division. Thirdly, there are factors that cause blood vessels to grow. Finally, there are some blocking microRNAs that may reduce the normal inhibition of de-differentiation.

This chapter is about the history of regenerative medicine, and my thesis is that MSC exosomes represent a significant inflection point in the evolution of that field. It is like Stephen Jay Gould's punctuated equilibrium, where suddenly things change quickly when a new paradigm is introduced.

Prior to the use of MSC exosomes, which began around 2018, doctors had traditionally relied upon a Faustian bargain to treat painful and worn-out musculoskeletal problems. They had only two choices: use steroids or cause inflammation.

For decades, when you had pain, the doctor would inject steroids into the area. Injection of local anesthesia only lasts hours and, therefore is useless for most cases. Nerve ablation is a somewhat barbaric last resort to just destroy the fire alarm without putting out the fire but in some cases, would be considered an option.

That said, the use of corticosteroids was somewhat ill-conceived despite being the standard of care and a reimbursable procedure. Yes, corticosteroids can decrease inflammation in the short term, but they don't necessarily stop the cause of the inflammation, and they are generally toxic to the structures that we are trying to help. In one study comparing saline versus steroids, the steroids resulted in *more* loss of cartilage than placebo.[2] It is also known that injecting tendons with corticosteroids can cause atrophy and rupture of those tendons.[3]

Likewise, putting steroids into the epidural space may somewhat alleviate pain for a short time, but there is a lack of evidence of efficacy according to the Cochrane reviewers of science literature.[4] Generally, corticosteroids are toxic to the tissues that produce bone and also the collagen-containing structures like discs and ligaments between vertebrae. Finally, despite lumbar epidural corticosteroids having never been FDA approved and even being the subject of a 2014 FDA warning for risk of "loss of vision, stroke, paralysis, and death", these injections are the de facto standard of care and are reimbursed by insurance.[5]

DON'T JUST DO SOMETHING, STAND THERE

As a former surgeon with bills to pay, I understand that in some cases, the intervention with a procedure that may provide relief is often an easy choice. Despite the knowledge that steroids and gels like hyaluronic acid have never been shown to improve long-term outcomes, we can't just stand by and do nothing, right?

In the non-surgical specialties, they sometimes have a different philosophy and may try to mitigate without procedures. The phrase "don't just stand there, do something" is inverted to "don't just do something, stand there" because, with time, the body will often restore balance and heal on its own. We sometimes called it "tincture of time" or "benign neglect" but as we would often say intraoperatively, sometimes "the enemy of the good is the search for better". If we simply do nothing, often the body will improve on its own, presumably using exosomes and native stem cells. But if those stem cells are old and worn out, we may have a non-inflammatory condition which we will call "osis".

OSIS – NOT ITIS

When I was training to do ultrasound-guided joint injections, one of my colleagues was a rheumatologist. She mentioned that in most cases of elderly people with "water on the knee," she would aspirate the knee fluid and send it to the lab only to find that there were no significant inflammatory white blood cells inside. Instead of arthritis (inflammation of the joint), she was finding **arthrosis**: the non-inflammatory description of aging in joints. If the problem were inflammatory, as with infection or autoimmune diseases like rheumatoid arthritis, you would expect to see a lot of inflammatory cells, right? In those cases, corticosteroids could actually be helpful.

If a person is an avid tennis player and has pain on the lateral elbow tendons of the arm, then they are likely to have problems with the extensor carpi radialis. But again, the problem is not an "itis" or inflammation as much as an "osis". Yes, there is inflammation that may be alleviated with steroids, but you also run the risk of atrophy of those tendons after injection because of the toxicity. Because it is a known complication, the doctor doesn't receive criticism if the steroid injection procedure fails to help the long-term functioning and even results in tendon atrophy or rupture.

As we will see in Chapter 11, if you damage a rat's knee cartilage, the biopsy will show senescence in the cartilage.[6] In the process of trying to repair, the stem cells' repeated copying without adequate telomere recovery between cell divisions causes replicative senescence. So, the final common pathway for joints and tendons is arthrosis or **tendinosis** (worn-out tendons). Although inflammatory arthritis and tendinitis may contribute to the progression to "osis" states, the uncomfortable truth is that steroids are the opposite of what is usually needed in older, damaged joints and tendons. But since we don't get paid for just standing there and people are suffering, we do it anyway despite the lack of evidence that they are effective.

YOU ARE PRACTICING REGENERATIVE MEDICINE WITH-OUT A LICENSE

If we consider what differentiates us from machines, it is the simple ability to regenerate our own parts. When a car has been used for too long, the belts fray and rupture, the tubing leaks, and brake pads wear down to the metal. But when a young person with plenty of stem cells gets injured, they marshal their MSC exosomes to induce the local stem cells into producing new tendons, cartilage, and blood vessels. There may be no detectable problems afterwards, but the body, and its aging stem cells, remember and keep score.

I treat a lot of older people, and they often wistfully recall the glory days of contact sports, falls, multiple injuries, and partial healing. Throughout life, damage is accumulating and even in the best cases, recovery is not likely to be reestablishing 100% of original strength, despite the patient not feeling pain or limitations. The exception to this rule is muscles, which grow and strengthen to beyond 100% via their own specific **satellite cells** (the muscles' stem cells). But hypertrophied muscles attach to bone with vulnerable tendons and let's not forget that using those stronger muscles puts more wear on joint surfaces and overstresses the normal ligaments that bind the joints as well. Despite feeling mostly okay in youth, the accumulation of damage can still occur, especially in athletes with strong muscles exerting unusual forces.

PROLOTHERAPY

The early years of regenerative medicine were characterized by a relatively medieval technique known as prolotherapy. A hypertonic sugar solution would be introduced, causing cells to osmotically explode and produce localized damage. The damage would cause inflammation, which would then bring in MSC stem cells to the injured area as well as activate the local MSCs in the capillaries. Those "medicinal signaling cells" release exosomes that will instruct the immune cells to switch from inflammatory to regenerative, and they stimulate the local stem cells to multiply and perhaps even act more primitively for a brief time.

So, if we cause cells to explode, cause inflammation, bring in stem cells to shut down inflammation, and then begin repair by secreting MSC exosomes, why can't we just "cut to the chase" and forego the damage, inflammation, and stem cell recruitment? Instead of hiring musicians, transporting them to the venue, and relying on them to play, what if we could just hit a switch and play the music from a prerecorded source to get the cells to dance? Although some practitioners still advocate the use of prolotherapy, a Cochrane review concluded there was no strong evidence to support its use in low back pain.[7]

PLATELET RICH PLASMA: PROLOTHERAPY WITH A TWIST

A beloved method of regenerative medicine for the last two decades has been the use of platelet-rich plasma (PRP). The technique involves extracting the patient's blood, spinning it with a centrifuge, and then using the layer of the stratified blood that forms between the red blood cells below and the platelet-poor plasma above.

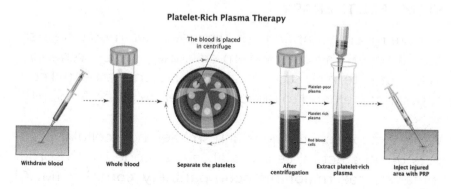

5.1: Platelet Rich Plasma (PRP) Methods

From listening to patients, the results of PRP injections are mixed. In many cases, there is improvement, and it is often quite dramatic and affordable. On the downside, it may require multiple treatments and is painful as a result of the intended inflammation. The theoretical problem with this technique is to be found in the post-care instructions. Patients are told they cannot use anti-inflammatory meds like aspirin or ibuprofen after PRP because the process is based on inflammation.

Why is this a problem? Well, if we know that inflammation can cause local tissue disruption, then we are gambling that the net effects will be positive despite the damage that can ensue. The summoning of MSCs that will then dampen the inflammation by releasing exosomes is what we are mostly relying on. That said, there are other growth factors from platelets and their own exosomes that can give us an extra benefit. But if we are primarily relying on PRP to cause inflammation and then provoke MSCs to secrete their exosomes, why not just use exosomes from a younger cell and in higher numbers? Also, if you speak with PRP practitioners, they will concede that the older the patient, the less effective the PRP tends to be. This may be related to the reduced amount and quality of the growth factors and exosomes that older platelets are making.[8]

STEM CELL THERAPY

A more recent weapon in the regenerative medicine arsenal has been the use of stem cells themselves. When we talk about stem cell therapy, there are some essential concepts that we need to understand before going forward.

While exosomes are the much smaller, non-cellular products of cells, actual cells are always encoded with something we call **major histocompatibility complex (MHC)** antigens/proteins on their surfaces. This system gives your cells a specific set of proteins that work like a secret handshake between them and your immune system. All your cells share the same MHC antigens.

The use of the same species, but non-self stem cells is referred to as **allogeneic** (pronounced al-oh-juh-NEE-ik). If you receive a transplant of an organ, they try to match the major MHC antigens as closely as possible, yet you still have problems because eventually, your immune system will reject those foreign cells. To delay this, transplant patients must take immune-suppressing drugs. Because allogeneic stem cells are recognized as foreign, your immune system will quickly destroy those cells.[9] While they are still alive, they secrete MSC exosomes, so they can produce some positive results. But why not just cut to the chase and just give exosomes?

When it comes to **xenografts** (pronounced ZEE-nuh-grafts), which are also allogeneic transplants from *different* species like sheep, studies show even less survival. In one study between pigs and rats, there were no cells that survived beyond seven days, even in immunocompromised hosts. In other words, other than the transient release of exosomes before the cells are cleared, those cells have no chance of surviving and a limited lifespan inside you.[10]

As for allogeneic human donations, which are commonly offered as off-the-shelf treatments, the results seem mixed. I have heard from patients that they do work to heal many conditions, but my gestalt is that response rates are about 50/50 and that, often the benefits tend to wear off over time. Again, if there is any benefit, it likely relates to the transient secretion of exosomes before the immune system clears them, so the question arises again: why not just use exosomes that have no MHC antigens and are never rejected?

Also unclear is how much inflammation is caused by hunting down and clearing the foreign stem cells.

When you use your own stem cells, it is called an autograft and is **syngeneic** (pronounced sin-jeh-NEE-ic). This is preferable but there are some caveats that we need to discuss. Firstly, unless you have saved cord blood or saved placental stem cells from your birth, you might need one of two procedures: a bone marrow biopsy or a liposuction. That said, there are some overseas clinics that claim that the MSC, the hematopoietic, and endothelial stem cells can all be extracted from your regular blood if you pretreat the patient with **GM-CSF (granulocyte-macrophage colony-stimulating factor.**[11, 12, 13]

A bone marrow biopsy is typically done by introducing a wide needle into your posterior pelvic bones and sucking out some of the marrow. It is not exceedingly painful, but there is the risk of any invasive procedure and its anesthesia, which is usually only local with or without light sedation. The problem is the FDA has deemed that as soon as you start playing with them to increase their numbers, you have violated their "minimally altered" standard, as we will discuss further in Chapter 10. That is why only clinics outside the US tend to offer the extraction of those MSC stem cells and their clonal expansion (doubling them repeatedly to make exponentially larger numbers).

While the appeal of having your genetically matched stem cells is clear, there is some execution and contamination risk whenever you rely on labs to do their jobs properly. If you're an older person, as with PRP, your MSCs and their exosomes would likely be less potent than those from a newborn placenta because of epigenetic gene silencing and perhaps even less efficient energy production and protein translation. So, having stem cells that were extracted while you were in your 20s might provide greater benefits.

The question that no one can definitively answer in vivo is whether the reintroduction of your extracted stem cells leads to engraftment (taking root) and mesengenic change (becoming the specific required tissue type) with any high level of efficiency. What seems fairly certain is that as long as they remain in the area of administration, there is no reason to think that they wouldn't also produce the desired exosomes to effect repair by stimulating local stem cells.

LIPOSUCTION FOR YOUR KNEES?

A common procedure in the US is the use of liposuction to extract tissue which contains some of the stem cells that we desire. In 2022, the US FDA filed a lawsuit against U.S. Stem Cell Clinic, LLC; the case is in appeal, as we will discuss in a later chapter. With the help of collagenase and mechanical techniques, the procedure yields what is known as the **stromal vascular fraction**. By centrifugation, this pellet, or heaviest part of the extracted fat is isolated and as you can see, it contains some rare stem cells, fully differentiated cells, and some that are in between (progenitor cells).

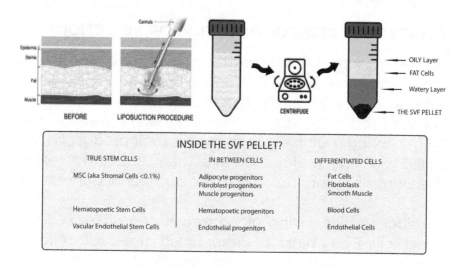

5.2: The Stromal Vascular Fraction "Pellet"

Because the FDA doesn't trust the clinics doing the liposuction to isolate, verify, and clonally expand (make repeated copies) of the pure MSC populations, the practitioner simply puts all of the above pellet ingredients back into the patient. For example, a liposuction is done, the aspirate is centrifuged, the SVF pellet is extracted, and then that mixed cell population is injected into a knee, for example.

The reintroduction of syngeneic cells may provoke some kind of prolotherapy inflammation and, therefore, attract more MSCs. Still, the actual purity and numbers of the desired MSCs delivered from the SVF are estimated to be less than 0.1% of the cells.[14] The use of collagenase (a tissue disruptor) to extract pure MSCs can be dangerous, but there is also a technology to mechanically isolate MSCs with saline as well.[15] Both these techniques for increasing yield might run up against the "minimally manipulated" FDA condition for homologous tissue use. So, if we believe that the primary method of beneficial action of MSC stem cells is mediated through their exosomes, why wouldn't we just use the exosomes and avoid the risk and expense of liposuction and MSC extraction?

WHAT ABOUT RISKS OF INFECTION OR REJECTION?

For the exosomes that I use, there is only one pre-Covid19 donor and they tested that donor placenta for 47 different diseases as well as the presence of bacterial endotoxin in each production run. There are exosome makers who claim pooling multiple donors makes their product better. Still, if you have multiple donors, the risks of undetected infections rise proportionally to the number of donors.

Consider the life-saving blood transfusion of packed red blood cells. Every batch of donor blood runs a risk of infectious transmission and can be rejected by the immune system because of minor surface proteins that are not the common AB or Rh Factor ones. But there is no reason to think that someone else's red blood cells wouldn't carry the oxygen needed for your cells while they last.

Remember when I told you that cells are like people and exosomes are just their language? Well, when it comes to exosomes, they are not like cells in one very important aspect other than being 1/300th the size: they don't have the major histocompatibility complex (MHC) surface proteins that serve to identify self from non-self. For that reason, there is no known mechanism by which your own immune system could "know" that it didn't make them, so they have the same effects in you as they would in the newborn baby that made them.

To emphasize the importance of being young, let's consider the phenomenon of scarless healing in fetal surgery. For reasons that are not entirely clear, when you perform open heart surgery on a fetus and allow that fetus to gestate and be delivered at full term, they often are born without scars.[16] The reasons may relate to more or better stem cells, higher quality exosomes, or less differentiated skin.

Given that you are already practicing regenerative medicine without a license by making your own MSC exosomes, the question then arises: would you rather have your old and limited number of exosomes that are not doing the job, or would you rather have a newborn stem cell's exosomes in higher numbers since your body can't recognize them as coming from an allogeneic source?

PEPTIDES

The use of specific peptides, which are delivered freeze-dried and then reconstituted for injection, has become popular in recent years. Although the anecdotal benefits are notable, in general, they don't seem to get the same immediate and potent results as using MSC exosomes and are reliant upon a specific biochemical mechanism rather than the natural symphony of many signals contained in nature's own repair toolkit (i.e., MSC exosomes). The FDA has also been active in shutting down many of the sources and distribution of these unapproved peptides, so their adoption and use are subject to regulatory ambiguities in many instances.

ADVANCED GENETIC TECHNIQUES

Although people get excited by the newness surrounding technologies of induced pluripotency (i.e., Yamanaka factors) and gene editing with CRISPR-Cas9, I don't believe they will be widely successful. Because the former inefficiently introduces an irreversible de-differentiation using oncogenes, there is the risk of teratomas but also of malignancy. For CRISPR-Cas9 to be effective, we must risk damaging existing genes. We cannot safely incorporate these methods for human use.

You may have detected a strong bias in this chapter against what other doctors use for regenerative medicine, and that is a fair critique. But if you were to speculate as to what the best method of regenerating and healing your damage would be, would you choose one protein and pathway, gene mutation, creating irreversible primitive cells, introducing a mishmash of cells from your fat, taking a non-matched allogeneic stem cell, or causing inflammation with PRP or hypertonic prolotherapy?

No. You would likely conclude that if mother nature, in all of us, deemed it wise to use MSC exosomes to repair you, then the safest and most effective method would be just to use what she gave us from a newborn source of MSCs in high numbers.

LIST OF SOME COMMON MSC exosomes proteins and mRNAs

Here are some of the many components expressed in MSC exosomes. According to one study, their songs of regeneration may feature over 170 miRNAs, 304 proteins, and many other mRNA contained in them.[17] Here are just a few of the overrepresented notes in these songs of healing:

miRNA-34a and miRNA-146a: convert M1 inflammatory macrophages to M2 regenerative type

miRNA-100 – inhibits immune cells from attaching to blood vessels

VEGF (vascular endothelial growth factor) – promotes new blood vessel growth

IGFBP/types 1,2,3,5 (insulin-like growth factor binding proteins) – carries and potentiates actions of IGF (insulin-like growth factor)

GDF11- (growth differentiation factor) enhances stem cell DNA repair

GDF15- decreases inflammation, influences apoptosis and cell growth and repair

TIMP1&2 (tissue inhibitor of metalloproteinase) – helps limit tissue destruction

SCF – (stem cell factor) – increases survival of blood-producing stem cells

SCF-R (stem cell factor receptor) – a receptor for SCF (stem cell factor)

GM-CSF (granulocyte-macrophage colony-stimulating factor

BMP-5 (bone morphogenetic protein 5) – induces bone and cartilage growth

GH (growth hormone) – stimulates cell growth and reproduction

HGF (hepatocyte growth factor) – promotion of epithelial cell replication and migration for new vessels and tissue regeneration

Insulin – promotes glucose uptake by cells

OPG (osteoprotegerin) – inhibits the cells which normally absorb bone

There are so many more that we could mention, and they are not randomly expressed in the MSCs exosomes. Although the condition in which the MSCs are producing exosomes can be changed to modify the output, we are quite far from understanding the many notes, harmonies, and motifs expressed in this cellular symphony. If you feel that using a complex mixture of powerful biochemical signals is dangerous, then you should take it up with Mother Nature because this is what your own cells are using to repair every single day.

Chapter 6

THE WORLD OF EXOSOMES

**I don't know anything about music theory at all.
Zero.
But I don't really need to.**

—Amos Lee (musician)

In this chapter, we are going to explore a bit of how exosomes are made and isolated. More importantly, we will expand the thesis that exosomes represent the fundamental way in which cells communicate with each other. To support this argument, we will first discuss the "bad exosomes." By the end, we will discuss some of the "good exosomes."

HOW TO EXTRACT EXOSOMES

Exosomes are everywhere, although until a few years ago, no one was looking for them because of their size and our ignorance of their importance. Again, scientists dismissed them as cellular "poop" instead of cellular communication.

If you eat a raw salad, you are eating plant exosomes, and yes, you are expressing plant proteins at some low level. If you drink unpasteurized cow milk, you are expressing cow proteins. At least in the case of cows, most of those proteins are nearly identical to your own, so there is nothing to worry about.

Although I am not privy to the exact details of commercial exosome production, we can infer some of the more critical steps from the scientific literature. First, you take one of the master cell bank vials (a frozen vial with identical MSCs that were isolated, verified, and frozen years ago) and thaw it to produce a working cell bank. These stem cells are allowed to reproduce by doubling to sufficient numbers to produce enough exosomes. If you allow them to exist and double for too many months, they will also undergo epigenetic gene silencing, telomere erosion, and senescence, therefore producing lower-quality exosomes. That is why constant sampling and quality control are needed to validate the health of your working cell banks.

The cells are growing and secreting exosomes inside stackable flat, pentagonal plastic flasks with screw-top openings which are about the size of a Gideon's Bible. The cells grow best in humidified air at 37 ° C, 5% CO_2, with a special stem cell nutrient medium containing FGF-2 (fibroblast growth factor) that is changed every 2-3 days.

- 37 °C incubator with 5% CO_2
- MSC Fluid Medium + FGF-2

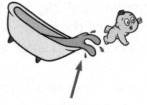

- Filter the bathwater for exosomes!

6.1: Stem Cell Culture Flasks

In older techniques, ultracentrifugation was commonly used, but these days, they have tangential flow filtration to do the trick. Because of the size exclusion, anything larger than the desired diameter in nanometers is not able to enter the filter and become part of our collected sample.[1] If they can mass produce two nanometer computer circuits for their chips, you don't think they can mass produce these filters?

If you force the schmutz inside solution directly into the size exclusion filters, they clog like a sink washing your golden retriever. But as shown in the cartoon, if you flow the solution tangentially, the small stuff that we want can drop into the filters more easily. There are also other types of filtration (e.g. track-etch) that can be used to enhance the yield of the MSC exosomes and exclude unwanted contaminants. But the main thing we are accomplishing is getting rid of the larger cells and unwanted extracellular vesicles, like the larger apoptotic bodies or microvesicles.

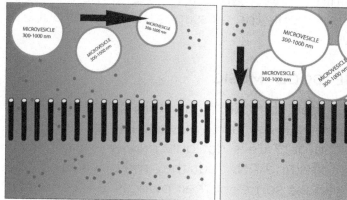
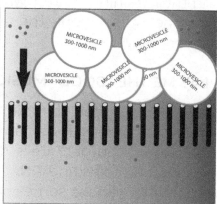

Tangential flow filtration
(150nm pores)

Dead-end filtration
(will get clogged)

6.2: Tangential flow filtration vs. Dead-end filtration

Remember that exosomes are like those supermarket toy capsules. Once you have your exosomes, you need to take a sample and melt the phospholipid bilayer with a soap known as Triton X-100 or something else to melt the phospholipid bilayer spheres to release the toys from within the balls without significantly damaging said toys.

Now, you send the contents to a lab to identify and quantify the proteins, messenger RNA, and microRNA (blockers) that you have inside the toy balls. But that is like taking all the notes in Stravinsky's score and placing them on a histogram. Two thousand E flats? One thousand B flats? Okay, we might gather some idea of what key we are in, but we need more information to know the scales, harmonies, melodies, motifs, and, most importantly, the mood that the music creates in the listener or dancer. Since it was a ballet, the permutations of how the dancers moved are as potentially diverse as the field of choreography itself. If we assume that they are classically trained in ballet at the Mariinsky theater, that is one thing, but what if the dancers are from a Burmese folk dance troop? Indeed, the cells and their training matter when it comes to the effects of exosomes; it is not only the messages that matter but the dancers as well.

PLAY ME THE "GOOD" MUSIC

Sadly, people often think in binary terms, like "good" or "bad". If you asked a musician to play you the "good music", what would you get? Cells not only receive signals from exosomal proteins and RNA, but they may, in a sense, be responding with exosomes of their own, as in a conversation. Much of the research into exosomes has been looking at cancer, and there are many thousands of articles attempting to discover the relationship between malignancy and cell communication via exosomes. To complicate matters, we can assume that there are good and bad things happening simultaneously.

In a nutshell, scientists found that once they started looking at the "bathwater" from cancer-affected patients, they found known proteins that contribute to known behaviors like altered immunity, decreased cell contact inhibition, increased vascularity, and a myriad of other pro-cancer behaviors. Studies have shown that the exosomes from a cancer patients' serum share immune suppressive traits and encourage metastasis.[2] On the other hand, exosomes from someone recovering from cancer might help fight progression in someone who is struggling.

The same principle applies to other diseases such as liver cirrhosis, and kidney disease.[3,4] The implication is that when cells are acting badly, they are listening and/or making "bad music." The conditions of developing many diseases may be related not only to the deterioration of the gene expression (epigenetics) and the so-called senescent phenotype (a vague and inclusive term for the behavior of the cell) but also to musical improvisation between members and monitors of those cells. To reach better understandings, we may need to reimagine diseases as emergent, ecological phenomena created by these musicians, dancers, and venue managers of the body.

Unfortunately, papers don't easily get published unless they name just one or two SPECIFIC proteins or mRNAs. Because a musical theory doesn't exist to discuss biochemical "chords," scientists try to find specific known signals and then allege that the entire clinical environment and disease are attributable to those two notes. But if we consider that Western music consists of only twelve semitones, consider how many biochemical "chords" we could play with thousands of proteins!

For those musicians reading this, the key of C major has seven notes. When you play C and G, you suggest C major. If you add the E in between adjacent C and G, then the triad of C+E+G is even stronger as a unique chordal identifier of

C major. Now add the D, and you have C9, which, to some, might sound dissonant. But if you are a jazz lover, you are just getting started. The addition of more notes to a chord makes for internal tension but also more complex meaning.

What I'm suggesting is that when you analyze what is inside "cancer" exosomes, but you only name one or two proteins to the exclusion of dozens of others, you are never going to understand the music on its own terms.

So what? So, instead of trying to deconstruct "The Rite of Spring" by Igor Stravinsky by finding the numbers of E flats and B flats in it, we need to watch the audience members and dancers for their emotions. In the simplest terms, we could either waste time arguing and reverse engineering the contents of liver exosomes in a person recovering from cirrhosis, or we could assume that they are not having a net negative effect and just extract them for use as a therapy to help others with cirrhosis. Of course, taking the extra step of analyzing their contents will help us build a cellular music theory for future reference.

While some among us may want to trust a drug company to synthesize each of the exosome proteins and RNAs in their precise ratios and then deliver them into a bespoke exosome, the lowest risk procedure would probably be to isolate and replicate the cirrhosis-resistant liver cells and just capture, validate, and use their exosomes in people who are struggling. That is because there are many opportunities to introduce errors when you try to make biologics in a laboratory setting.

My personal bias is that Mother Nature is going to be better at bioengineering than we are for the foreseeable future. Although we congratulate ourselves for billion-dollar molecules or antibodies that may block or mimic a single molecule or pathway, any honest physician or scientist will acknowledge that there are many bypass pathways that are not affected and that untoward side effects can ensue.

The implication of trusting Mother Nature is that someday, we may have cultures of different cell types and not just the universal soldier/doctor of the MSC. In other words, if you have a neurological problem, then you may require the exosomes from a neural stem cell. That makes sense, right? If you have a problem with your retina, the MSC exosomes would help, but there may be more specific crosstalking exosomes produced by the retinal stem cells that could work more specifically. Again, we don't have enough knowledge of cellular music theory to know for sure, but there is a sound, logical basis to believe that organ-specific stem cells might produce even more helpful exosomes for organ-specific diseases.

Let's put it in a simpler context in terms of analogies. If I wanted to eat chicken eggs, I could analyze the contents of the eggs, create artificial shells, and then manufacture the whites and yolks in a molecularly and spatially correct manner and package them into my artificial eggshell. Or I could just get some hens and let them do their thing. Would you rather eat my artificial eggs or the ones laid by hens?

So where are we now? There are thousands of studies and more emerging that are starting to reveal some of the ways in which cells communicate with exosomes. It turns out that most of the conditions we think of as wellness or disease may just be like some kind of inscrutable dance party happening between cells. If they are young, healthy, and well-behaved, it is a movable feast of fun. If they are diseased and rowdy, there could be property damage, arrests, and trips to the ER.

WHY MSC EXOSOMES?

The reason much of the research on exosomes focuses on MSC exosomes is that they are easy to extract and known to stimulate regeneration. The theory, logic, intuition, and experiments all support using the thing that Mother Nature herself prefers. The isolation of MSCs is possible from a variety of sources, but we prefer the most potent ones from a newborn placenta, which are "adult" with regard to lacking the dangerous pluripotentiality of embryonic stem cells.

I mentioned that exosomes don't have MHC surface antigens that cells do, so they can't be rejected. If natural injury causes inflammation, which brings in your old MSCs, which secrete 100% of their poorer quality exosomes, then why wouldn't we prefer many times more exosomes from a younger, more potent source?

The proof that younger is better comes from the origin story of the first producer of exosomes for commercial use. Its founder and lead scientist was trying to grow MSCs from an older woman to help her COPD. Those older cells wouldn't divide, so he couldn't make enough copies for her. But when the bathwater from a teenager's MSCs was poured onto the septuagenarian's stem cells, they did start to divide robustly. Of course, younger cells would have responded better, but the key lesson was that with the right signals from younger cells' exosomes, the older stem cells could still be coaxed into acting young and dividing.

So, with MSC exosomes, we have a universally effective and science-based method to decrease inflammation and regenerate cells. Once the exosomes are harvested from those plastic flasks, they can be tested for those 47 infections, checked for the known surface proteins that confirm MSC exosomes, tested for their contents, resuspended in sterile normal saline, frozen for future use, and cleared from quarantine. Your provider has to maintain them frozen as well because companies that use freeze-drying will lose the majority of their exosome viability after reconstitution.

Why are exosomes more expensive in some cases? Well, I could sell you eggs off the back of my truck for a fraction of what you would pay in a supermarket, but you wouldn't know if I personally harvested them or even if I have my own chicken farm, training, safety inspections, expiration dates, salmonella outbreaks, bird flu, etc. You can assume that the cost to maintain high-quality control through every production run is not only the cost of the skilled employees, the facilities, the regulatory compliance, and the loss of revenue from substandard exosomes; it also includes research and development into new kinds of exosomes and very costly FDA trials and research collaborations with academic institutions and contract research organizations.

There are manufacturers who say they are producing exosomes when, in fact, they may just be grinding up placental tissues or gathering amniotic fluid from multiple donors, filtering the debris, and not even confirming the presence of the usual surface markers that validate MSC exosomes, to say nothing of ruling out 47 known infectious disease.

Chapter 7

___

HOW TO BE IMMORTAL

For the soul, there is never birth or death.
Nor, having once been, does he ever cease to be.
He is unborn, eternal, ever-existing, undying, and
primeval.
He is not slain when the body is slain.

—Bhagavad Gita 2:20

For the last nineteen years, I have been thinking about aging. Like most younger people, I never gave it much thought until I was 37 years old. That was when my father was afflicted with brain cancer. I took to the internet and the scientific literature to understand what theories were out there and considered them all using reason and intuition. Since then, I have continued to learn, attend seminars, meet gurus, receive feedback from my patients and social media followers, and generally remain open to all theories while critically considering them at the same time.

What I've concluded is that most people only see the trees in the forest that pays them. Instead of relying upon self-proclaimed experts to do the thinking for us, let us bravely deconstruct the question of immortality armed only with our own carefully considered science, logic, and intuition.

I DON'T WANT TO DIE

This simple statement is a core value for most sentient beings when they are in a relative state of homeostasis. But what does it really mean to be alive and to die? The realm of science fiction has allowed us to conduct useful thought experiments and indeed the question is a non-trivial one. We assume on our scale of being that to have a heartbeat, to be conscious, and to have free will are some of the essential aspects of being alive as a human.

But what if I told you that you can undergo surgery and be on cardiac bypass for a while, and no one would really consider you as having died and come back to life? So, it's not really the heartbeat that defines your existence.

People fall into comas all the time, although not as often as they do in television dramas. During that time, the imaginative areas of the brain are not very active, and the subjective experience of consciousness is debatable. When they awaken, we don't consider them to have been dead and then alive again.

As for free will, I only bring it up because the technology to emulate people's speech, mannerisms, general themes, and banter is advancing rapidly via emulator programs such as the language-model artificial intelligence known as ChatGPT4. Personalities such as Albert Einstein and Michael Jackson can be emulated with a passable degree of accuracy. If you could one day cheat death by creating a program for yourself to emulate your consciousness, would that constitute a trapdoor escape from death? Perhaps without justification, most people would conclude that without the free will to act like someone else besides your programmed persona, it would be just a parlor trick and wouldn't constitute cheating death.

So to be alive, we can temporarily lose our heartbeats or consciousness, but we need to emerge with some kind of free will and not just exist as an emulated persona.

"SHE'S RIGHT THERE, NEXT TO TED WILLIAMS"

In my travels, I met a gentleman in the cryonics community who mentioned he had talked his mom into posthumously being cryopreserved. Before you dismiss this method of immortality, let me first say that there is a lot of reason to believe that such a thing might be possible.

Although the intricacies of what constitutes human consciousness are poorly understood, there is a strong argument for some kind of "solid state". What I mean is that unlike the transient memory of RAM (random access memory) that exists in computer chips when there is electrical current available, there are memories and functions of the brain that are stored in physical form, like the ones and zeros on a traditional hard disc drive or the newer "solid state" drives.

It is uncertain how successful the future thawing and restoration of consciousness will be. To be fully functional, the thawing, repair, and reconstitution of a human brain sometime in the future will likely be challenging owing to the damage from freezing, cell rupture, chemical alterations, and other unknown unknowns.

That said, we know that an embryo that has been frozen for twenty years can be thawed and gestated into a normal newborn person. That would suggest that extreme cold and metabolic stasis do have the effect of halting the structural, genetic, and epigenetic decrepitude that comes with the notion of an **"arrow of time"** (i.e., time moves only in one direction).

But what exactly is the "solid state" of human conscious-ness? Certainly, having largely intact neuroanatomical structure is key. But an entire field of knowledge is lacking here because it appears that the shape mimicry proteins known as **prions** play a significant role in encoding mem-ory and they are still poorly understood.[1] Nevertheless, hav-ing a relatively preserved and carefully frozen brain and body, one thousand years in the future, might just buy you a ticket to some form of meaningful immortality.

That said, we should also consider that the brain and head are supposed to be connected to a body. Many choose the discount option of not freezing their entire body because they think the data is all in the head. Fair enough, but there will certainly be a lot more work and errors if scientists must reconnect a new body to old nerves, vessels, and lymphat-ics. And can you imagine the physical pain when they first reconnect your old brain to a new body? And who is donat-ing their old body to you in the future? I answered that in my sci-fi graphic novel although perhaps many don't even consider the ethics of it when they sign up for head-only cryonics.

THE IMMORTAL SOUL

For most humans living on the planet, the concept of an immortal soul is not just an article of faith but an intui-tively felt and believed part of their existence. Let's just say for the sake of argument that your soul is immortal and that it has been formed by other souls or that it becomes other souls. It doesn't necessarily have to be a monad, one for one, because quite frankly, the new souls have to come from somewhere and not everyone can be Cleopatra and Napoleon, unless we do a little subdivision. So, the good news is that if there is an immortal soul, then you are all set. But, I suppose the good news could also be considered the bad news because some believe your "karmic" actions will determine the kind of life (or even species) that you will reincarnate as.

COMMON-SENSE IMMORTALITY

Although the phrase above may seem like an oxymoron, it is really meant to be deadly serious. With all due respect to religion and notions of reincarnation, which I don't refute, most people would NOT consider having an immortal soul, cryopreservation with faith in future scientists, or consciousness emulators, to be truly achieving immortality.

In fact, when I've given lectures on aging, I sometimes ask the audience "who would like to live to 120 years?" and there are rarely any hands that go up. Why is that? Because science, logic, and intuition tell us that the entropic process of aging will render a life at 120 years to be unpleasant and burdensome to ourselves and others.

When it comes to common sense immortality, if you frame the question differently, most hands will go up: "Who would like to be 120 years old if you could have the mind, body, and health that you had when you were 20 years old?" So that is what common-sense immortality means...having negligible aging while maintaining optimal health and wellness.

This is where the economists come in with their Malthusian warnings. I remember once having the audacity to question my mentor, Dr. Rosenfield, in his premise that population explosion would be a critical problem. The truth is that in this year of 2023, as in every year before and every year after, human population is an economics problem, not a moral, sociological, or cultural one. In every so-called "developed" nation, the expense of raising children has resulted in negative population growth. Now there's an oxymoron for you: negative growth.

In contrast, in places where children can be used for child labor, there is population growth because it takes a while for the kids to understand that they are being exploited and there are no laws against it.

In the end, it is problematic to decide who gets to be born, but I'm fairly certain there are some megalomaniacs who wouldn't mind doing just that. More concerning is the ability to engage in ectogenesis as described in Aldous Huxley's *Brave New World* or as in the cloned warriors of Star Wars, Boba Fett. It is possible to have babies without parents now. Just a sperm, an egg, and a plastic bag with nutrients. If it is deemed that the nuclear family, religion, nationalism, or any other form of identity are hindering social order, then it might be an aspiration of corporations to birth and raise their own "children", unencumbered by those legacy institutions.

NOW I'M BORED *AND* ANNOYED, DR. PARK

For some of you, the previous paragraphs may have succeeded in boring and annoying you rather than provoking thought, so I will return to our premise of how to be a common-sense immortal. In this regard, we are faced with two essential concepts: the arrow of time and the inevitability of entropy.

To the philosopher and his heir, the scientist, the "arrow of time" implies that as we currently perceive it, time has a direction, and it moves forward at roughly one second per second. Although we can change the way we perceive the past, and that can make all the difference in the present and future, the actual material events that take place in the physical world don't easily tend to reverse themselves.

The second great force is that of entropy. In other words, it takes effort and energy to maintain order, but eventually, like the temples of all past empires, they invariably fall to ruins. Why do I bring this up? Because, unlike the guru influencer who stated your DNA never changes, in fact, it does. It is estimated that from the original 3 billion base pairs (or letters) of your human genome, there is a typographical error of about one in every three cell divisions. That is impressively accurate, but it is not perfect. So you can never hope, with existing genetic hardware, to avoid drifting away from your original software that was bequeathed by that original sperm and egg.

If you think, as I do, that this excellent, nearly "lossless" reproduction is impressive, then you are going to be disappointed in the epigenetic fidelity. Copying the methylation silencing and acetylation promoting software marks from mothers to daughters is nowhere near as accurate and introduces more entropy into the system. One old study estimated about a 1% error rate.[2]

Luckily, we have three other forces in the cellular pantheon that can rescue us, as well as a trickster on par with Odysseus, who invented the Trojan Horse. To combat the forces of time and entropy, we have the forces of homeostasis and rebirth.

On an island outside of Mumbai, there is an ancient statue known as the *trimurti*, which enshrines the fundamental Hindu concept of a triad of primal forces known by the god names of Siva, Vishnu, and Brahma. The best way that I can explain cell biology would be by invoking these deities for use as analogies. All through your life, when there are serious problems, cells can commit suicide (**apoptosis**) or undergo immune-mediated killing. This force is represented by the god **Siva** (pronounced SHE-vah), the destroyer.

The god of maintenance is **Vishnu**, the preserver. I believe the reason why I have a full head of black hair at 56 is because I have taken a telomerase activator every night for 16 years. No other incredibly healthy lifestyle hacks other than sleeping a lot. No hormones. No other supplements. We know that humans born with a defect in any of the three critical elements involved in telomerase-mediated telomere lengthening will face premature aging. We also know from different species of animals and plants, that higher rates of telomerase activity are associated with longer lives and that faster attrition of telomeres is associated with shorter lives.

The final god is **Brahma**, the creator. Of course, the stem cell is the creator in the truest sense and we all started as a single fertilized egg: one totipotent (all-powerful) cell that would gradually produce more differentiated and specialized stem cells and their daughters. Yet, as the Yamanaka experiments and other isolated instances of guided de-differentiation via blocking microRNA have shown us, cells can sometimes go back and become more primitive for a time. If it is unbridled, it can look like cancer. But if it is controlled, it can look like a salamander leg regrowing or a person recovering from a stroke.

Siva — Vishnu — Brahma

p53 -apoptosis
Immune destruction

Telomere length
Autophagy

Telomerase
Stemness

7.1: The Hindu *Trimurti*

So, I'm saying that aging and illness arise from the effects of loss of genetic and epigenetic data integrity that is primarily natural but accelerated by telomere attrition as occurs with overuse (over-copying). The loss of telomeres causes depletion of the stem cells (loss of Brahma) via cell suicide (Siva and the p53 suicide pathway). Practicing better health habits as explained in my book, *The Telomere Miracle*, can enhance telomerase and like Vishnu, maintain your cell functioning.

So, what about the trickster Odysseus? Well, someday soon, when we are able to better understand the ways in which cells become other cells, we can purposefully use them to make replacement parts. So, the most logical thing to do is forget sheep, allogeneic donors, or even liposuction, and instead freeze your stem cells for future scientists to make bespoke replacement parts for you and replenish your Brahma. Do you think it more likely that future scientists will be able to microscopically reconnect thousands of nerves, vessels, and lymphatics of your thawed head to a decapitated future body or that they will discover the signaling pathways and genes/proteins to repair and regenerate your organs using stem cells?

The original equipment manufacturer's genome is mostly pristine after being thawed, so the problems with genetic and epigenetic errors haven't had a lifetime to be introduced as in your current state. That's what a clever Greek would do and that's what we probably should do if we are really interested in engineering immortality.

Even though the supply wouldn't be literally infinite, it would be close. That's because cells start to age and degrade only when they live and copy themselves outside the freezer; so the "younger" stem cells can be replenished to a nearly pristine state ad infinitum.

I just told you how we can easily create effective health and wellness for centuries and you're probably now thinking about economics. Don't worry, everyone does it. But I'm just saying, it's not that difficult to understand and certainly not in the realm of science fiction.

EPILOGUE- MITOCHONDRIA AND BRAIN LINKING

I believe that currently existing autologous newborn stem cell harvesting and banking, coupled with future stem cell scientific breakthroughs, is the most logical and promising method to cheat death. But I feel I need to address two other popular ideas among immortalists: mitochondria and consciousness transfer.

In 2008, I self-published a graphic novel called *Maximum Lifespan* in which a scientist cheats death using both of those technologies. (SPOILER ALERT) The man cloned himself twice and in the first embryo, he put too much non-human mitochondria, and the clone son experienced premature aging. But in the younger clone, he put a better ratio of protozoan mitochondria and the aging was very slow.

The reason for this plot device is that although many people believe that mitochondria play a central role in driving aging, the likelihood is that they are the cart, not the horse since they are comprised of healthy-at-birth robust structures with a simple circular DNA. They are endosymbiotic bacteria that live by paying their energy rent inside most of our cells.

In my story, the ability of the mitochondria to cause cell suicide after p53 activation is hindered by the non-compatibility of the protozoan-specific messaging with its human host cells. The suicide program can't be activated in the ageless clone because the scientist engaged in **symbiogenesis** (making new life by combining two species).

The second way in which the scientist cheats death is by tricking his son into entering a sensory deprivation tank, drugging him with dissociative hallucinogenic drugs, and electronically "swapping" consciousnesses and bodies. Now THAT is the stuff of science fiction. Although there were residual "ghosts" in the hijacked shell of the now possessed son's body, I don't really believe my own story premise that an entire personality with its memories, traumas, neurotic fallacies, and libidinous tendencies could be modulated, demodulated, and then overwritten onto another human consciousness. If you want to read my graphic novel in eleven languages, see the OTHER WORKS BY THE AUTHOR section at the end of the book.

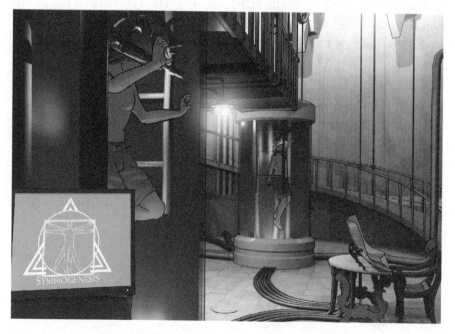

7.2: *Maximum Lifespan* consciousness transfer

Nevertheless, there are people who believe that even without the "wetware" of a human body with all its prions, neurons, hormones, and **qualia** (consciousness states), that consciousness coul be digitized, stored, and transferred and not just emulated via language model AI. For me, this is an intuitive non-starter because talking to faux Whitney Houston and enjoying her avatar's hologram singing will never reach the verisimilitude of having a genuine and heartfelt conversation with a real person about how she sometimes hated having to play the persona of Whitney Houston, the superstar.

The British computer scientist to crack the Nazi Enigma code was Alan Turing. He proposed that if a machine could convince a reviewer that it was a genuine human, then it would pass his Turing Test. For you and me, there is a discernable difference between real humanity and an emulation and it is a primal feature of the species. It is never going to be "*cogito ergo sum*" or "I think, therefore I am." It is instead "I feel it, therefore I am." I feel it in my gut, I feel it in every fiber of my being, or I experience it in every *chakra*.

For those of us who are alive, we may lack the language to express it, but no parlor tricks of software and prosthetics will ever convince us that we don't know what it is to be alive. I believe a real human would have so many more intuitive and unpredictable ways of assessing humanity that the pretender would have to resort to tricks to deal with the myriad of improvised ways you could challenge a program to prove its alleged humanity.

So would you like to live to 120 years if you looked and felt like a 20-year-old? Most likely, yes. So let's focus our attention on achieving that goal for the rest of the book.

Chapter 8

"OSIS" IN THE BODY

**Sports teach you how to be quick.
Injuries teach you how to slow down.**

—Yao Ming (professional basketball player)

We have begun to understand that while we are machines, we do maintain the magic of stemness that, for brief periods, can act like a regenerative force. Unlike cars, we last longer despite wear and tear because of those effectively immortal stem cells. But because of entropy, those stem cells become error-ridden by genetic and epigenetic errors. Over time, if the errors are severe, then the Siva of self-destruction will take place, and the local stem cells will be depleted.

Over a lifetime, aging leads to "osis," not "itis." Osis is not really a word, but rather a suffix, yet it describes a common process. Mechanical damage, hypertonic sugar, infections, and autoimmune attacks are just a few causes of "itis." Inflammation of anything can be described by adding this suffix; in the kidneys it is nephritis; in the liver, it is hepatitis; in the heart muscle, it is myocarditis; and so on.

A common finding when you get an ultrasound or MRI of a painful tendon (fibrous connection of a muscle to a bone) is what radiologists describe as tendinosis. These are "worn out" tendons from aging, damage, and incomplete repair by the locally depleted and dysfunctional stem cells. Aging is primarily not causing tendinitis, or an acute inflammatory process. If you ask someone in their 90s what hurts, they might reply "everything, everywhere, all at once." An ultrasound would show increased fiber spacing (gaps), calcifications, thickening, and changes in the appearance of the normal tendon. An MRI might show irregular density, fluid, and actual tears. Common sites of tendinosis are the rotator cuff in the shoulder, the tendon below the kneecap attaching to the tibia, the lateral elbow, and the Achilles tendon.

As I mentioned before, if you try to treat a tennis elbow with steroids, you run the risk of causing more harm by inducing atrophy because the steroids are toxic to the cells.[1] While pain may be resulting from inflammation, often the actual cause of the problem is just aging/overuse, which are, in terms of stem cell telomere attrition and depletion, really the same problem.

We find the analogous problem within joints and their cartilage-lined surfaces. When trauma, aging, and overuse result in incompletely repaired joints, like the knees, hips, and shoulders, we encounter what is known as arthrosis, not arthritis. Again, shortened telomeres lead to osteoblast aging and eventual depletion.[2] Of course, the availability of Calcium, parathyroid hormone, estrogen, Vitamin D and K2, weight-bearing exercise, and the balance of osteoblastic (creating) to osteoclastic (destroying) activity play essential roles as well. But as with all the niches in your body, the aging of the stem cells in the subchondral bone that is producing the joint cartilage surfaces leads to thinning, increased friction, and joint wear. There may be periods of inflammation associated with this, but in general, the fluid from a knee that is old and has arthrosis doesn't have many inflammatory white blood cells. Interestingly, the tendency is to interchangeably call joint disease "arthritis" rather than arthrosis yet somehow tendinosis is usually referred to as tendinosis.

In Chapter 11, we will cover the study done on mice where they intentionally damaged the knees and then examined the tissues later. What they found was that the surgical damage resulted in premature aging and senescence of the cartilage-producing cells.[3] So, if you cause injury and provoke cell replication to try to heal, then the cell divisions come too rapidly without telomere recovery between cell divisions. This leads to rapid depletion (Siva, the destroyer) of the stem cells (Brahma, the creator) without the necessary telomerase activation (Vishnu, the maintainer) between divisions. The telomeres shorten, and the stem cells become old, leading to arthrosis, not arthritis.

YOUR ELECTRICAL WIRING IS RARELY REPLACED

Another problem that occurs with longevity is nerve damage. In many aspects, the loss of neurons is inevitable because they rarely can regenerate and must last a lifetime. If you purchased a television 70 years ago, would it surprise you if some of the electrical components wore out after that time? What often contributes to nerve damage or neuropathy is not actually mechanical damage or internal cellular failure but rather vascular damage. In other words, nerves are served by tiny blood vessels. When the tiny blood vessels are damaged, the nerves die. That is why diabetics, who have small vessel disease from excessive sugar, often develop neuropathy, which is experienced as lack of sensation in the feet.

SUMMING UP THIS BOOK

At the present time, we don't have any approved medications or procedures that can regenerate the "osis" compartments of tendons, joint cartilage, bones, or small blood vessels. Those who want to "do something instead of just standing there" can try steroids, but again, those are toxic to the previous tissues. If you have true inflammation, as from an autoimmune disease or gout, then short term use of steroids is okay. But, in most overuse/aging cases, they are not helpful but your doctor doesn't want to just stand there and do nothing. In the case of joints, sometimes they put a temporizing hyaluronic acid to help with pain, but this won't actually regenerate cartilage.

As we mentioned in the chapter on regenerative medicine, there have been some successes with inflammatory prolotherapy and PRP injections, as well as from stem cells from autologous or allogeneic sources.

In general, we rely upon our own body's release of MSCs and their exosomes to mitigate "osis" where it can by stimulating local stem cells. When we are young, we have a lot of cellular and functional reserve in our tendons, joints, and bones. When I say reserve, I mean those structures are mainly in their original, undamaged, full capacity. With time, everyone ages, all stem cells acquire genetic and epigenetic problems, and those stem cell compartments and their tissues degrade.

Up until now, I have performed exosome treatments in over 1800 instances in over 700 encounters, in almost 400 distinct patients. While I can't say that everyone has had a positive response, in general, I would say that around 70% of those treated experience significant improvement in their pain or loss of function by simply administering more of what they are already trying to make. We give MSC exosomes from a newborn placenta's stem cells, and the patients' local stem cells seem to respond as they are programmed to do. If you are healing at 100% of your capacity at your age, the idea is that giving many more exosomes from a newborn source of MSCs will multiply that by many times.

Whenever I do an injection, I explain that the procedure is not FDA-approved, nor standard of care, and may have no benefits. We also discuss the alternatives and common risks, but in general, the injections are well tolerated because there is no mechanism to reject them, they are highly anti-inflammatory, and we are just powerfully enhancing your own body's natural conditions for regeneration.

In this brief chapter, we introduced the idea that most of the aches and pains that you have are the result not of acute inflammation but rather of aging and its ally, overuse. Of course, acute trauma can also incite incomplete repair that also results in tendinosis and arthrosis. In the later chapters, we will explore some anecdotal evidence that exosomes can help to mitigate and reverse these problems that we all accrue during a lifetime.

Chapter 9

THE IMMUNE SYSTEM

For every complex problem there is an answer
that is clear, simple, and wrong.

—H.L. Mencken

There are few things more complicated than our immune system. Imagine a parliamentary government in which no party has a majority. Now add open borders, natural disasters, embargos on importing medical supplies, multiple internal and external terrorist groups, high rates of crime and arson, and a tourist brochure stating this is a peaceful place to visit and live. That is life for your unappreciated and amazing immune system.

If we deconstruct the analogy, having a "coalition government" implies that different aspects of the immune system need to cooperate to get things done; if one part tries to "go it alone," we have problems. "Open borders" implies that through breathing, eating, sex, orifices, and skin, pathogens are constantly being introduced, and some can take up residence and cause problems. "Natural disasters" might be exposure to radiation or **aplastic anemia** (non-production of blood cells) after viral infection. An "embargo" implies that without hematopoietic stem cell replenishment, your naïve T-cells (or improvisational blank keys to new threats) deplete as with that old Dutch lady, as a result of telomere attrition.

"Internal terrorists" include cancers, attacks on friendly cells (autoimmunity), human herpesviruses numbered 1 through 8, which hide in our DNA, harmful flora living in the gut, respiratory, skin, or genital systems, and various intracellular critters from the bacteria that cause Lyme disease to syphilis.

"External terrorists" include intestinal worms, protozoans that cause amoebiasis or malaria, insect bites, venomous animals, bacteria that cause the plague, leprosy, diphtheria, pertussis, and tetanus, numerous viruses, and the omnipresent mold and fungi that surround us.

"Crime and arson" implies that our immune responses must address cells that get out of line and also put out "fires," like inflammation and hypersensitivities. The "tourist brochure" is meant to imply that people have an expectation that they will be healthy and safe despite the reality of how complex and challenging it is to maintain homeostasis amidst the constant peacekeeping that is demanded of the immune system.

Although the preceding paragraphs may have filled you with a slight dread, the good news is that for most of our lives, we feel well and have enough naïve T-cells to have a sound immune system. We harbor latent herpesviruses, but we might only get a cold sore after an 18-hour flight delay. A mosquito bites us, and we itch, but we don't go into anaphylactic shock. Countless bacteria live in our colons and vaginas, but they serve to keep more dangerous ones away. When our immune-supporting Vitamin D and K2 is low in the winter, we get cold and flu viruses, but we shake it off in a day or two with some sleep and antibodies memorized from the last time we had that cold. If we need a bit of help, we might take an antibiotic for amebic diarrhea we got drinking from a stream or we can take hydroxychloroquine for malaria. If we inhale some tree pollen, we sneeze, but we generally don't develop welts on our skin and wheezing. And even when we develop microscopic cancers or bacterial blood infections from being lacerated, your immune system usually has got it all covered. Immune function is a bit like customer service; you only notice it when it's bad.

While it is pretty easy to understand how tennis elbow occurs in those simple collagenous fibers made by local stem cells, the diseases that arise from immune dysfunction are more challenging to understand. That said, we know that one of the most important aspects of being alive and resilient is having a functioning immune system. Recall the Dutch lady, van Andel-Schipper, after living 115 years, only had two remaining out of 11,000 blood-producing stem cells, and even those were mutated.[1] A child will rarely be impacted by a cold virus but it could prove deadly to someone with such little immune reserve.

The problems that can arise from having even a perfectly normal immune system are numerous. It is believed that if we don't get exposed to enough germs as small children, there are higher rates of allergies.[2] So, a healthy immune system is one that has created a library of remedies to life's challenges, and yet can also downregulate after clearing those challenges. If we don't downregulate, we can develop hypersensitivities known as allergies. If we start to misinterpret certain of our own cell types as foreign, we'll get autoimmunity. This may be triggered by energetic mutations (UV or EMF), viral genome insertions, random gene mutations that come from telomere shortening, and toxins in our food, environment, and medicines.

Since we usually harbor up to eight human herpesviruses that can never be eradicated because they hide in our DNA, the immune system is tasked with keeping these at bay, but this causes more rapid depletion of its "blank keys" (**naïve T-helper cells** aka **CD28 positive T-cells**). A great example of a culprit that lives with us for a lifetime is CMV (cytomegalovirus or HHV-5). There is ample evidence that fighting this chronic infection is a primary force behind immune aging, which likely accelerates aging generally. Thankfully, the use of TA-65 appears to mitigate this depletion.[3]

As with the storing and regeneration of our own MSC stem cells that I described in Chapter 7, there is a solid case to be made for storing hematopoietic stem cells for future use. Instead of succumbing to loss of immune competency, we could periodically recharge the immune system with fresh, naïve hematopoietic stem cells in the future. The AIDS from HIV and just getting old are essentially the same process of HSC depletion. We need to recognize that walking the arrow of time causes metabolic and replicative activity that results in entropy and a lower-case AIDS (acquired immune deficiency syndrome). That is why, with both AIDS and aging, we find cancers that don't usually occur in the immune competent. But even when comparing cancer patients by their HIV status, researchers found that the epigenetic ages of tumor cells were greater in those with the HIV.[4]

There are few things more complicated than the immune system. Nevertheless, let's understand a few concepts that will serve us well. After presenting this crash course on the immune system, we will explore three subtopics: inflammation, the basic ways of recognizing friendly cells, and how MSCs interact with the immune system to promote regeneration. You don't really need to master these concepts to get value out of this book, but it wouldn't hurt.

THE HEMATOPOIETIC (blood-producing) SYSTEM

The cells in our blood system are mostly produced in the bone marrow. There are three basic components of blood: platelets, red blood cells, and **leukocytes** (white blood cells). On the surface of all cells, we can have self-identifying MHC molecules, types I and II (Roman numerals), which we will explain during the section on adaptive immunity below. Just know that MHC-I are the self-identifying proteins that are found on all cells except red blood cells. MHC-II is found only on cells that present fragments of enemy proteins in order to train the immune system to destroy them.

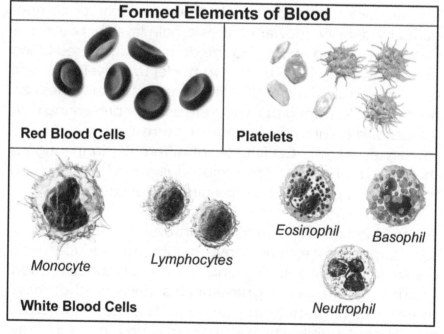

9.1: Formed Elements of Blood[5]

Platelets are cell fragments without a nucleus that can combine with clotting factor proteins to form blood clots when needed, such as in the case of skin lacerations or even tears in blood vessels. Think of them like straw for the self-assembling concrete that are the clotting factors. Defective clotting factors cause easy bleeding through the disease of hemophilia.

Red blood cells (aka erythrocytes) also lack a nucleus, and they contain densely packed molecules of hemoglobin, a four-part protein molecule that carries oxygen from the lungs to the body via arteries and returns carbon dioxide back to the lungs using veins. Red blood cells do NOT have MHC-I surface identifying proteins but instead AB and Rh types that we test to match donors to recipients.

Leukocytes ("white blood cells" or WBCs) are called that because when you spin whole blood to separate compo- nents by density, they appear as a pale layer between the clear plasma fluid above and the densely-packed red blood cells below. They have their own nuclei to actively produce proteins and also have MHC-I antigens. But certain ones also have the MHC-II antigens which are used for presenting new threats and training the immune system. On the surface of leukocytes, we find **CD (cluster of differentiation)** antigens that help us understand the cells' origins and functions, and they can also have biochemical binding functions as well.

White blood cells can be divided into categories by micro- scopic appearance, genealogy, function, and surface mark- ers. Let's list them all in descending order of representation. About 50% are called **granulocytes** because they have three types of granules inside them; the most numerous are the **neutrophils** which kill bacteria and fungi. Secondly, we have the **eosinophils,** which specialize in fighting para- sites, and finally, the **basophils**, which release histamine to help clear things you are allergic to.

Agranulocytes are the other nucleated cells of the immune system and they come in four types: 25% are **T-lymphocytes/**

cells ("T" stands for thymus), 10% are **B-lymphocytes/cells** ("B" for bone marrow), 5% are **Monocytes,** which are anti-gen-presenting cells that can become **macrophages** or antigen-presenting **dendritic cells** when they migrate to tissues, and lastly, 5% are the **natural killer cells**.

Remember the Dutch lady's only two surviving hemato-poietic stem cell types (HSC) from depletion? That is aging by depletion caused by telomere attrition, gene silencing, and whatever else causes aging. In time, Siva the destroyer trumps Brahma the creator, if Vishnu the preserver is sleeping. Here is a working genealogy of what one hema-topoietic stem cell can become, and by understanding the paragraphs above, you should know all her descendants as well.

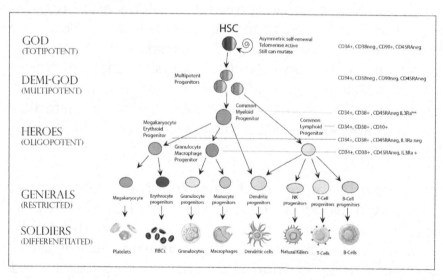

9.2: The descendants of the HSC (Hematopoietic Stem Cell)[6]

Before we explain the main players of your immune sys-tem and how they work, let's mention some of the meth-ods those players use. Firstly, we have the **complement system**, which is a number of interesting proteins made in the liver that can cause a sort of "martial law" to help respond to pathogens, especially when they've been coated with antibodies (more on those below). Another system that becomes activated during infections and inflammation are the **leukotrienes**, which are organic molecules whose synthesis is blocked by aspirin and ibuprofen; they also raise the level of alert and are largely responsible for those fevers and aches. **Histamine** release by blood **basophils** or tissue-localized **mast cells** can also produce inflammatory symptoms like sneezing, swelling, itching, and redness.

Critically important for immune function are **cytokines**, which are the signaling proteins that are responsible for coordinating immune responses. They do this by attracting leukocytes, modulating their behavior and level of aggressivity, and causing them to multiply and undergo **B-Cell or T-Cell activation** (more on this later). You may have heard of some of them with names like IL-4 (interleukin 4), interferons, and TNF (tumor necrosis factor). Some diseases that are characterized by too much immune function, like autoimmune diseases, can be mitigated by designer antibodies called "biologics" to block these cytokine pathways.

Okay, now to the heart of what the immune system is and how it works its magic. But first, let's distinguish between the innate and the adaptive systems. The innate system is one that works without **anamnesis**. For those lovers of Greek, anamnesis means "not forgetting," and the anamnestic response is what we have when the cells remember an old enemy and can mount a proportionally stronger response after learning that enemy's surface proteins.

The innate immune system is comprised of the natural killer cells, which can kill fungi and cells that are compromised by cancer, viruses, and intracellular bacteria. There is also a system to recognize generic threats such bacterial cell wall **lipopolysaccharide (LPS or endotoxin).** LPS triggers a nonspecific inflammation that can escalate to sepsis and the activation of the adaptive immune system. This LPS nonspecific triggering is an example of PAMPs (pattern-associated molecular patterns), and there are also DAMPs (damage-associated molecular patterns) which signal host cell destruction and a need for a rapid innate immune response to act as a "clean-up crew" when there is a lot of host cell death. Both the PAMP and DAMP responses trigger nonspecific inflammation.

THE ADAPTIVE IMMUNE SYSTEM

Although algae, plants, insects, and fungi rely only on nonspecific, innate mechanisms like those we just discussed, animals with backbones (vertebrates) have adaptive systems that can respond to and then remember previous threats so that they can more easily overcome them on future encounters.

To accomplish that, they need lymphocytes known as B-cells and T-cells. The "B" stands for bone marrow, where they mature, and these specialized cells can make up to 2000 antibodies a second each when they are activated to become **plasma cells**. B-cells can also be of the **Memory Cell** type, meaning they remember old threats and can be used to rapidly respond to those old enemies if they come back.

T-cells are so named for the thymus, a small, spongy organ under your sternum and above your heart. You already know that all blood components are made in the bone marrow, but T-cells have to attend training by going to the thymus to become mature. There, they learn how to recognize the self through positive selection, but they also learn how not to kill friendly cells through negative selection. They are differentiated by their different roles and by surface proteins known as CD (cluster of differentiation). There are two general types of T-cells: the **CD-4 positive T-Helpers** and the **CD-8 positive T-Killers** (aka cytotoxic).

Although we categorize them as separate, the innate immune response can lead to an adaptive one in most cases. Let's say you get meningitis from a common bacteria known as *Neisseria meningitidis*. The LPS cell wall triggers an inflammatory response using the complement system. As the bacteria are being destroyed, they release proteins that can be swallowed up by ameboid macrophages, which, in turn, activate the adaptive immune system.

When an enemy like a bacterium is swallowed up and then digested by a macrophage, the fragments of proteins can be "presented" alongside the MHC-II antigen on the cell surface, and they can also be belched out of the macrophage into the surrounding environment for other cells to recognize as foreign. When the macrophage presents the enemy protein fragment with its MHC-II molecule, it can be recognized by a specific **TCR (T-Cell receptor)** on naïve CD4 T-helper cells, causing that T-cell to then become **activated.** An activated T-Helper cell can then start to conduct a rapid, specific expansion of B-cells to form neutralizing antibodies in the plasma cells targeting that specific enemy protein shape.

Remember the blank key analogy? Well, your ability to respond to new threats can be directly measured in your blood by checking for CD28 positivity. In order for a naïve CD4 T-helper to become more powerfully activated, it

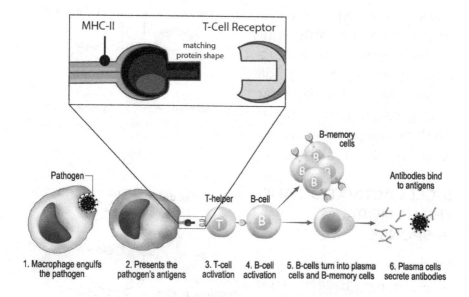

9.3: Macrophages activate T-Helpers

has to have its CD28 surface receptor co-stimulated by a macrophage's B7 surface protein. This is like saying to the T-Helper cell "This is not a drill! We have to handle this at Defcon 1"

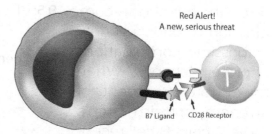

9.4: Macrophage B7 Ligand Co-stimulation of CD28 on the naïve T-Cell

CYTOTOXIC T-CELLS AND THE HIJACKED YACHTS

When cells are affected by viruses, cancer, or intracellular organisms, they can place a specific enemy antigen next to the MHC-I surface protein to cry for help. It would be like a hijacked personal watercraft writing "SOS" on its flag for the Coast Guard to see. They are not "professional" antigen-presenting cells like macrophages or B-cells, but it still gets the job done. When a shape-compatible TCR on a CD8 Cytotoxic T-cell matches the antigen+MHC-I hijacked cell's cry for help, the cytotoxic cell can become activated, expand in numbers, and hence efficiently kill other hijacked cells that also present this antigen on their cell surfaces along with the MHC-I self protein.

B-CELL ACTIVATION AND THE HUMORAL RESPONSE

In the lymph nodes, you have naïve B-cells that have surface B-cell receptors that are reshuffled through genetic recombination to offer a variety of possible combinations of protein "shapes." When the digested fragments of an enemy protein match a naïve B-cell's B-cell receptor, the B-cell will ingest that protein and then join it to its own MHC-II protein before presenting it on the cell surface. In doing so, the B-cell has now also become an antigen-presenting cell and it can also ask the T-Helpers

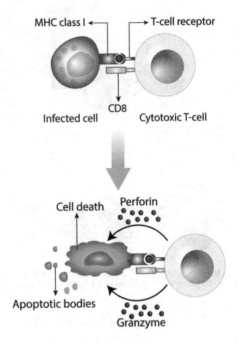

9.5: CD8 Cells Kill Hijacked Cells

T-cell dependent b-cell activation

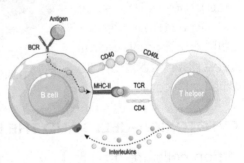

9.6: B-Cells can cause CD40 Co-stimulation in T-Helpers

for help by using the MHC-II + antigen method but also the co-stimulatory **CD40 ligand** (binding protein). This is analogous to the macrophages' use of B7 ligand to CD28 to create a co-stimulatory "Defcon 1" signal.

T-CELL DIFFERENTIATION

You may not understand the following, but it is included for completeness. After a naïve T-helper cell is activated, it can become one of many types: T-helper 1 (Th1), T-helper 2 (Th2), T-helper 17 (Th17), and T-regulatory (Treg) to name a few.

IL-12 and Interferon gamma promote **Th1 differentiation,** which causes the production of more IFN-gamma, TNF-A, IL-18, and IL-2. **Th1 (T-helper, type 1)** cells stimulate **macrophages** to fight intracellular pathogens by focusing on phagocytosis (swallowing pathogens).

Under the influence of IL-4 and IL-2, the T-helper will tend to become a **Th2** type, producing IL-4 and IL-5 (among other cytokines). The IL-4 greatly assists a humoral response by inducing rapid clonal expansion (specific cell copying by rapid division) of themselves (the Th2 helpers). IL-4 will also induce rapid clonal expansion of the activated B-cells that have learned to fight a specific meningococcal antigen, for example. The IL-5 secreted by the Th2 cells also causes B-cell differentiation to plasma cells and memory B-cells. Therefore, Th2 phenotype (behaviors) assist in rapid expansion of the humoral system with antibody-mediated responses. It is also associated with dealing with parasites and allergens by expansion of numbers of **eosinophils**, by producing lots of IgE (the hypersensitivity antibody type), and by mast cell degranulation to secrete histamines. Th2 is active when you have atopic symptoms (asthma, eczema, and allergic sinusitis).

TH17

Under the influence of TGF-beta and IL-2, the naïve T-cell can become a Th17 type. Those Th-17 cells produce IL-17, IL-17F, IL-21, and TNF-alpha. The type of cell that is expanded by its activation is the **neutrophil,** so the Th17 phenotype is good at responding to extracellular pathogens like bacteria and fungi. These neutrophils can trap bacteria and fungi like Spiderman by spraying out their own chromosomes like nets![7]

Treg (T-REGULATORY)

The regulatory T-cells are also stimulated by TGF-beta and IL-2. They play a prominent role in downregulating inflammatory responses.

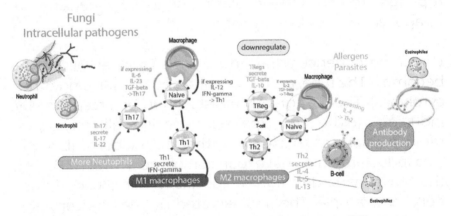

9.7: T-Cell Differentiation is Driven by Types of Threats

ANTIBODIES: THE FOCUS OF THE ADAPTIVE IMMUNE SYSTEM

You may wonder, "If you knew I wasn't going to understand the last few paragraphs, then why did you include them?" The main reason was to show that the cells use cytokines to change each other's fates, numbers, and functions. You also begin to see that understanding the music theory of cell behavior is complicated. When I said the immune system is like a parliamentary government, it is because all the many innate and adaptive ways in which the system can respond to threats are happening together and although some can be enhanced in importance during a specific challenge, the ultimate goal is to handle the invaders and then return to balance.

If you don't fully grasp how the immune system works, you are in good company. Scientists who devote their lives to this also struggle to find patterns and causal relationships to what is, after all, a balanced symphony of many different themes and motifs. I will try to extricate us from this section of the chapter with a simple reduction of what you need to know.

Thanks to physical barriers and fluids, friendly flora, innate inflammatory pathways, natural killer cells, and other adaptive lymphocytes, the healthy immune system (i.e., lots of naïve cells) can improvise a nearly infinite number of responses to whatever new pathogen it is faced with. Proteins have shapes that can be neutralized by rapidly produced, specific antibodies that coat and mark specific pathogens for clearance. Cytotoxic T-Cells can also detect and destroy hijacked cells, and finally, natural killer cells can clear virus or cancer-affected cells.

AUTOIMMUNITY

What happens when cells become trained to attack the host's own cells? We refer to that as autoimmunity, and the causes of it could be from gene mutation, viral triggers, or other unknown factors. If the above pathways are some-how convinced to recognize a friendly part of your immu-nologically-visible cell surface proteins, we can get various conditions such as insulin-dependent diabetes, thyroid dysfunction, lupus, multiple sclerosis, and even baldness.

MSC EXOSOMES PROMOTE M2 MACROPHAGES, WHICH ARE ANTI-INFLAMMATORY

Everyone knows that MSC exosomes play a crucial role in healing from injury, but exactly how do they do that?

There are hundreds of reasons we could guess at given the mRNA and protein contents of the exosomes, but let's try to identify some general trends.

Arabpour et al. showed that MSC exosomes appeared to cause macrophages to change from activated M1 to anti-inflammatory M2 subtypes. This M2 polarization resulted in fewer proinflammatory M1 macrophages that release TNF-alpha and IL-1beta. The M2 macrophages release more of the TGF-beta that is anti-inflammatory.[8]

Chen et al. confirmed that MSC exosomes provoke three major changes, probably because of M1 to M2 polarization: again, decreased inflammatory M1 cytokines of TNF-alpha and IL-1beta and also increased anti-inflammatory TGF-beta from M2 macrophages, and increased numbers of immune-suppressing Tregs.[9] TNF-alpha and IL-1beta are secreted by activated macrophages and other cells to increase the inflammatory response. The Treg cells are also down-regulators of the adaptive immune system.

Unfortunately, scientists struggle to create broad conclusions about what cytokines and cells are doing when, actually, they could be doing many things at once. That said, the M1 macrophages tend to dominate in early injury because they promote greater inflammation, which helps clear tissue debris and has antimicrobial benefits. We know from the chart below of the stages of tissue repair that a shift to the M2 macrophages corresponds to the post-clean-up rebuilding that comes after initial inflammation. This focuses on the downregulation of the immune response now that the injured site has been sterilized and debrided. The M2 macrophages, along with the other signals contained in the MSC exosomes, are going to oversee the rebuilding phase of tissue repair.

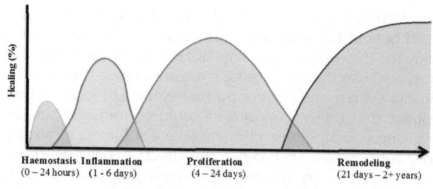

9.8: Tissue repair sequence[10]

Recalling Chapter 5 (A BRIEF HISTORY OF REGENERA-TIVE MEDICINE), we speculated that older methods like prolotherapy and PRP that cause inflammation are effective because they recruit MSCs to secrete their exosomes. When a person has a chronic injury like tendinosis, there is less concern over bacterial infection or partially digested cell debris, so we can jump right to the M2 phenotype and encourage proliferation and remodeling. In the case of using exosomes to enhance post-surgical healing, I tend to wait at least a week because the inflammatory phase does help to sterilize the wound that might have been contaminated.

In this chapter, we attempted to outline some of the major actors and roles of the immune system. Because of the Dutch lady and common sense, we understand that the process of aging and becoming more susceptible to illness are driven by stem cell mutation and depletion not only in the hematopoietic stem cells, but in all cells presenting their self-identities. As we become genetically divergent unto ourselves, more and more autoimmune diseases are possible. Because we must suppress but cannot eradicate certain human herpesvirus, the naïve "blank keys" are used up during a lifetime of keeping things like CMV at bay.

Recall that I told you taking allogeneic stem cells is of limited benefit because the immune system will clear them due to MHC-I incompatibility. But if they do have a benefit, it is because they do release exosomes while they are still viable. Even more concerning, however is a theoretical possibility that these foreign cells could engraft and survive, making you a genetic chimera (like a sphinx is a mixture of a human, lion, and eagle). The effects of having a divergent genetic identity living inside you would be unpredictable because there is no known way for them to pretend to share the host identity when their own MHC-I self-antigens are different.

Thankfully, the field of stem cell science may soon allow us to reverse-engineer and expand the dwindling numbers of our own genetically matched hematopoietic stem cells. But until that day, we must hold out and stay healthy. Without a doubt, one of the critical breakthroughs in achieving common sense immortality will be the ability to restore the strength and plasticity of our immune systems.

Chapter 10

EXOSOMES AS LEGITIMATE THERAPY

If money go before, all ways do lie open.

—Shakespeare, *The Merry Wives of Windsor*, Act 2, Scene 2

Before we embark upon this chapter, let's agree that nothing you are doing to stay alive has been FDA-approved. The thousands of proteins and pathways involved with breathing, digestion, elimination, urination, sleep, exercise- none of it has been approved by the FDA, yet they keep you alive. Do you think you should turn yourself in for practicing medicine without a license?

Scientists tell us that MSC exosomes are always working in our bodies but especially when we are injured and require regeneration. You are always using your own MSC exosomes, so administering more of them to be used in a homologous fashion could be considered like breathing deeper, exercising more, or getting better sleep.

A question that I'm often asked is: "Are exosomes FDA-approved?" A related question is, "If these work so well, why don't the drug companies push for them?" The first question is quite reasonable, but the second reflects a misconception about what the FDA is. We need to discuss intellectual property considerations regarding whether something natural can really be owned by anyone. We will also discuss the current position of the FDA regarding cellular therapeutics generally and exosomes specifically. We will explore the use of exosomes for the prevention of Covid-19. Finally, we will theorize about the possible benefits of exosomes to treat a host of other conditions, including genetic diseases and cancer.

WHAT IS THE FDA?

The US Food and Drug Administration oversees food production, medicines, and medical device regulation. By reviewing scientific trials that validate the safety and efficacy of new treatments it provides an invaluable public service that improves our lives in many ways.

That said, I am often struck by the resilience of patients who try to stay away from doctors generally. As we age, many people allow themselves to have medication after medication added to their regimens because they don't realize the doctor hasn't the time or the interest to manage and simplify what they're taking. Often, one drug begets a complication, and then the complications warrant a new drug. People gather more and more medicines, like decals on NASCAR vehicles. Few people embrace a healthier lifestyle and the advice of ancient Greek physician Galen, who said, "Let food be thy medicine."

In the case of foods, the production processes and facilities must follow guidelines and are subject to inspections. Other companies that produce products such as blood or tissue substances also must agree to be inspected and follow standard safety and production guidelines. If they are out of compliance, they can be sanctioned and shut down.

Devices for use as prostheses or in the case of surgery also must apply for the approval of the FDA, and this can be a costly endeavor.

In the case of therapeutic medicines, the process of obtaining FDA approval is a costly and daunting one. There are generally steps towards winning this approval, and those include an **IND (investigational new drug)** application, which is the permission to start testing in humans. After the IND is approved, the prospective drug developer must undergo three phases of trials. Phase one trials focus on safety and are smaller. Phase two assesses efficacy, usually in a randomized, placebo-controlled fashion. If the drug is safe and effective, the phase three trial compares the therapy to existing treatments. Note that if what we believe about stem cell exosomes is true, this three-phase model is largely irrelevant because there is such high reported safety, and often, there are no existing treatments to compare with.

If a drug is clearly safe and effective, then the costs to do an FDA trial might be less, but the costs are generally high for new small molecule candidates. According to one study looking at drugs from 2014 to 2018, the median cost was $985 million, and the average cost was $1.3 billion.[1] It would take a company with very deep pockets to make it through the process, although the twenty-year prohibition of generic versions can make it a lucrative prospect. Even for small molecule drugs or biologics (usually antibodies) that show minimal benefits, the insurance companies and government entities that pay for the newer treatments rarely consider the ethics of being overcharged and simply pass on the costs, despite perhaps having a negligible advantage over older therapies.

If you listen to the possible side effects of a direct-to-consumer drug advertisement, they are so grave and numerous that it sounds like a comic parody sketch. Sadly, FDA approval is never a blanket assurance of safety but rather a sort of "fig leaf" for providers and drug companies to protect them in case you are one of the unfortunate ones who become injured by using the product. In some cases, the untoward effects are common enough to attract class action lawsuits, and drugs are withdrawn from the market as a result.

There are many examples of problems with FDA-approved medications. Diethylstilbestrol was a synthetic estrogen approved for atrophic vaginitis in 1941 and was used "**off label**" (for a non-approved indication) to prevent miscarriage until its approval in 1947 for just that indication. Unfortunately, until its removal from the market in 1975, it was used despite no proven benefits and increased risk of uterine malformations and vaginal cancer. Another example of a drug that caused harm was a drug similar to aspirin called VIOXX, which was FDA-approved and then withdrawn when it was associated with a fourfold increase in myocardial infarction. There are reasons that pharmaceutical companies hire attractive sales representatives, and there are reasons that laws were passed against giving doctors free vacations and other gifts. The ability and willingness of a doctor to consider the safety of any new drug is influenced by their intellect, ego, ethics, and wisdom.

And just who pays for FDA approval? As a result of the 1992 approval of the "User Fee Act" by Congress, the majority (up to 75%) of the budget of the FDA is paid by the companies that submit applications. On the surface, that would make sense and prevent frivolous submissions, but imagine a private school where the students hand the teachers cash and then, after graduation, hire the teachers as highly paid board members. There is an ecosystem that exists between government regulators, drug company management, and lobbyists. There are very few examples of top people at the FDA who do NOT enter some form of lobbying or pharmaceutical/ device management. Relationships matter, and sadly, the same beltway revolving doors are found in most areas of commerce, such as weapons manufacturers, petroleum interests, banking, and professional organizations.

It is puzzling why some people believe that the government is altruistic and pursuing the greatest good for the public. Even more vexing is the willingness to believe that people will risk their own careers and influence to blow the whistle on bad ideas and bad players. The exception to the rule? Dr. Marcia Angell, former editor-in-chief of the New England Journal of Medicine, who revealed an uncomfortable opinion about falsification in academic and regulatory studies that she felt was rampant:

> *"The boundaries between academic medicine — medical schools, teaching hospitals, and their faculty — and the pharmaceutical industry have been dissolving since the 1980s, and the important differences between their missions are becoming blurred. Medical research, education, and clinical practice have suffered as a result."*
>
> —(from *The Truth about Drug Companies*)[2]

Often, a drug or device is approved despite a lack of greater efficacy or safety. Like a blockbuster movie with no discernable plot and ham-handed production, the show must go on so that the billion dollars invested in development can be recovered by captured payers and consumers before intellectual property protection expires. Once a drug's patent protection runs out, it can enjoy a second life as an over-the-counter medicine. In a breathtakingly shrewd and original move, the maker of Claritin for hay fever, Schering-Plough, granted Anthem (the owner of health insurer Blue Cross/Blue Shield) its request to the FDA to convert the antihistamine from a prescription-only to one that was available "over-the-counter." Although they lost years of patent protection, Anthem saved a fortune, and Schering-Plough also made a fortune from its huge direct-to-consumer sales.

So, what was the point of the preceding paragraphs? In many instances, the FDA is an efficient purveyor of safety and efficacy amidst therapeutic innovations and serves to validate new treatments that, when used wisely with the help of a healthcare provider, positively impact our lives. But by the same token, when there is money involved, there are many points of failure in the system that can result from data falsification, profiteering, and flexible ethics.

The main elephant in the room is this: if scientists claim that MSC exosomes are always present and increasingly activated when we have damage and need repair, how would someone go about getting FDA approval for this? Before I answer that question, we should consider actor Angelina Jolie and the case of the BRCA1 gene.

INTELLECTUAL PROPERTY AND BIOLOGICS

A company called Myriad Genetics tried to patent the BRCA1 and BRCA2 genes, which have long been known to be associated with higher rates of solid cancers such as breast and ovarian cancer. They used Angelina Jolie to raise awareness, and she used her own test results to justify pro-phylactic mastectomy and breast reconstruction.

The **USPTO (US Patent and Trademark Office)** had previ-ously allowed genes to be patented. The company alleged intellectual property over naturally occurring human genes, but this ownership was challenged, and in 2013, the

US Supreme Court unanimously ruled that such owner-ship was illegal. Even the company, years later, acknowl-edged the court got it right by stating, *"Myriad does not support patents on products of nature, including natu-rally occurring DNA and unmodified human genes."*[3]

The reason I bring this up is because exosomes that we can obtain come from a human stem cell line without an owner. For the exosomes that I currently use, a single donor placenta was given, free of charge, after a normal cesarean delivery. Now, if a company could create an immortalized MSC stem cell line, say using extra copies of telomerase genes, that might justify a patent and warrant intellectual property protection. But the problem is that all cell lineages in culture eventually acquire mutations and, therefore can become dysfunctional and non-viable because of telomere attrition and epigenetic gene silencing. The production of a Star Wars-like "clone army," if you will, would require mass production of very early reproductive stem cells and cryo-preservation followed by scientific validation of relative uni-formity across master cell banks. That may sound like a lot of jargon, so let me simplify it for you.

Whenever cells double, they must copy all their DNA, most of their epigenetic software, and split up the mitochon-dria and organelles (membrane-bound) organs between daughters. Although stem cells usually have telomerase to lengthen their telomeres, if they don't have adequate time or capacity, they can undergo replicative senescence as we discussed in Chapter 2. Even with errors in the 3 billion base pairs of our DNA occurring on average only one base pair per three cell divisions, there is always the capacity for ran-dom and potentially serious mutations being introduced every time a mother divides into two daughters. When the **PD (population doubling)** count is low, the cells are closer to the original. But if you allow stem cells to keep on doubling in a dish for many PDs, they can start to behave unpredictably and even act old or senescent. That is why a good exosome product would have to be thawed from an early PD master cell bank, expanded, and discarded periodically to prevent the older chickens from producing rotten eggs.

So, without the introduction of multiple copies of telomerase genes or anti-apoptosis genes, there would be no unique invention, and the ownership of exosome-producing cell lines would fall into a greyer area of a "utility patent" filed with the USPTO, which might involve methods of extraction and identification that a company could be reluctant to share. Generally, companies choose to submit to FDA approval and do not bother going through the USPTO.

FDA'S CURRENT STANCE ON STEM CELLS AND EXOSOMES

Because of the very broad mandate of the FDA to review all food, drugs, and devices, they don't have the manpower to regulate everyone who is advocating something in the world. Early on, when someone tore a knee ligament, they were presented with the option of not removing their own tendons to patch things up but rather using tissue from human cadavers. The use of **xenografts (non-human donors,** like porcine heart valves) is less desirable because they can be rejected more easily.

To regulate the use of these **allografts (non-matched, human donor)**, the FDA has a subdivision known as the CBER (Center for Biological Evaluation and Research) with guidelines known as CFR (Code of Federal Regulations) Part 1271. These sections outline the correct practices for isolating, storing, and implementing **HCT/P products (human cell and tissue-based products)**. The key theme in this section is that "minimal manipulation" must be done and that products should be for "homologous use." Since exosomes are neither cellular nor tissue, there is room for debate as to whether they are referenced. But the MSC exosomes made by a newborn placental MSC cell line should be exactly homologous to the ones that you would normally produce.

Because the science of stem cells and now exosomes is relatively new, the FDA has repurposed these guidelines to include cell therapeutics. They do conduct manufacturing site inspections to ensure cleanliness, organization, protocols, quality control, and safety. It is up to the companies themselves to create those protocols and procedures and to engage in the appropriate testing to rule out infections and confirm potency and purity. In a May 2021 interview with Dr. Peter Marks, the director of the CBER, he stated they were interested in MSC exosomes for immune suppression but that they were not unregulated Section 361 products because: "as they [the exosomes] are manufactured, they are more than minimally manipulated." I do not know what he meant by that, but here are the four criteria that need to be met in order to be outside of FDA purview under what's known as Section 361 of the Public Health Service act. They are:

- Not more than minimally manipulated;
- Intended for homologous use only;
- Not combined with another article; and
- Either the HCT/P does not have a systemic effect and is not dependent on the metabolic activity of living cells for its primary function, or if it does the product is for autologous use, for use in a first- or second-degree blood relative, or for reproductive use.

As you read in the previous chapter on regenerative therapies, I believe that the use of allogeneic stem cells should be largely deprecated based on their limited lifespan in the recipient, theoretical creation of genetic chimerism, and because their efficacy is mainly based on exosome secretion, which we can achieve without a cellular product.

The use of autologous stem cells is a more complicated topic to consider. I do believe that one's own stem cells can be isolated, stored in a frozen state, expanded, and repurposed. Furthermore, I believe that stem cell and exosome scientists of the future will do even better to help mitigate cellular and organ dysfunctions and disease by harvesting, storing, and then defrosting those autologous cells in the future so that they can secrete specific exosomes for specific purposes.

The problem I generally have is that stem cell science is not that easy to do. When liposuction is performed, there are many cells that exist in the stromal vascular fraction, not just stem cells. Making a single-identity stem cell extract is a difficult process. In order to create higher yields, they use collagenase (to break up connective tissue). Unfortunately, if the collagenase enzyme is not diluted and neutralized after its use, it can cause untoward effects, as evidenced in the case of stem cell injection into a patient's eyes, resulting in blindness from the collagenase.

The "minimally-altered" standard is there to protect us because, frankly, I don't believe most small clinics have the staff, equipment, and expertise to do what needs to be done to truly isolate, expand, and repurpose stem cells. There may be some clinics with those capabilities operating outside of the US, but the economics of personalized stem cell medicine, under the scrutiny of the FDA's minimally-altered standard, don't make sense. The FDA attempted to stop doctors from doing autologous stem cell transplants from liposuction when they sued, but the court did not rule in their favor.[4]

The case is currently under appeal, but the ruling of the judge was that, despite using collagenases and despite sending to a third-party lab for clonal expansion of numbers, **the autologous use of one's own liposuction-derived cells was not in violation of the CBER regulations**. Specifically, the judge ruled that procedures were covered under the SSP (Same Surgical Procedure) clause, that the product was not a drug, and that no interstate commerce was occurring.

It remains to be seen what the government's appeal will mean for the future of autologous stem cell use. In the meantime, we do know that according to Dr. Arnold Caplan, most of the benefits of stem cells come from their exosomes, and we still have access to those. There are multiple companies that have received approval to test their MSC exosomes for a variety of conditions, and if any of them succeed, at least a door for "off label" use may opening in the future.

Many drugs prescribed are done so in what is known as an "off-label" way and in some populations, that number can even approach 97% of the medications used.[5] That means the original FDA approval may have been granted for one specific disease, but given the knowledge, experience, and logic of a similar condition, a physician decides, hopefully, but not often with the patient's informed consent, to use a drug in a manner that it was not originally approved for.

COVID-19 SPIKE PROTEIN mRNA THERAPY

In 2020, it was claimed that a new strain of coronavirus began to affect people, creating widespread fear and reshaping public policy. Drug companies Pfizer and Moderna were assisted by an emergency use authorization by the FDA to approve two mRNA exosome products delivered by lipid nanoparticle (like phospholipid natural bubbles). As in nature, these artificial exosomes contained a synthetic mRNA message inside the bubbles that would be introduced into cells that they contacted. Operation "Warp Speed" showed some unprecedented skipped steps in the approval process, even resulting in the unblinding of the placebo group and giving them the active product, despite the fundamental negation of the study validity from doing that.

In the rush to approve, the notion of "don't just stand there, do something" was king. Since then, the original mRNA versions have lost their approval status in favor of newer versions, and the Johnson adenovirus version of the gene therapy for spike protein introduction has been removed entirely from the marketplace.

What is the lesson? If you are a massive drug company with allies in the FDA, any money-making product can skirt the normal processes that are intended to weed out the unsafe and ineffective. If you add legal indemnity to the approved new drug, you have a situation in which there is only economic upside with no risk.

So, since the Covid mRNA shots were artificial exosomes with a single mRNA synthetic analog to the SarsCov-2 spike protein, we can say that at least two exosomes are FDA-approved. Unfortunately, they are made in a lab and not made by natural human cells.

EXOSOMES BEING TESTED WITH THE FDA

There are several companies that allegedly produce MSC exosomes and have received approval for an IND with the FDA. Does that mean they will succeed? Not necessarily because trials cost money and not everyone can raise those funds.

Some of the trials listed on various commercial exosome websites include using MSC exosomes for the treatment of Covid, Long Covid, COPD, Crohn's disease, autism, infertility, acute respiratory distress syndrome (ARDS) and more.

Why are there so many trials proposed? Because in practice, people are reporting good results so there are some who feel that a trial using exosomes for various conditions would be successful.[6] Understand that the greater the positive effect, the fewer patients you need to prove efficacy and the more cost-effective the trials will be. People with real life experience are betting that exosomes will perform the way they did in anecdotal cases.

WHAT IF WE COULD TREAT GENETIC DISEASES AND CANCER?

Rarely, especially in genetically isolated populations, we find mutations in genes that are inherited. When cells have only one good copy, the random loss of the only remaining good copy can cause problems, especially when that mutation occurs in an immortal stem cell. In most cases, using exosomes to temporarily insert the missing mRNA might be nearly as good as having the normal gene. We hope that having too much of a protein from multiple gene copies wouldn't be a problem, like those elephants with twenty copies of the genetic proof-reading anti-cancer p53 gene.[7]

This means that for dozens of known and serious genetic disorders, scientists could easily produce the mRNA for a specific gene and introduce many temporary copies into an exosome. The result would be a temporary "cure" to hundreds of rare but known genetic conditions that have serious health consequences. This technology exists today. If they could introduce artificial Coronavirus spike protein via exosomes, then we can also introduce helpful mRNAs for proteins that people may lack due to their genetic inheritance.

What is more encouraging is that, in most cases, cancer represents the deletion of one or more important genes that control DNA integrity, cell division, contact inhibition, and suicide. In certain cancers, certain genes are commonly affected. For example, pancreatic cancer, which is quite lethal, usually has the same genes damaged. 90% have a KRAS mutation, and up to 74% have a p53 mutation, CDKN2A mutations are in about 50%, and SMAD4 mutations are in about 35%.[8] If we could put all four mRNAs into an exosome, we might have an off-the-shelf treatment for many pancreatic cancers. What if all our tax dollars went to academic centers that would treat patients with life-saving bespoke exosomes, free of charge, instead of funding ineffective new molecules that cost billions to bring to market?

So why don't drug companies work on these? Sadly, the answer is money. If drug companies cure genetic disease and eradicate cancers through temporary replacement of missing proteins, that would cannibalize their sales in other areas. Also, since the Supreme Court determined no one can own a gene sequence, owning mRNA-based exosomes therapies might also be an issue. Unfortunately, the greatest good for society and for patients is not what sets the agenda for new drug development.

This chapter has been an exploration of why human MSC exosomes are not yet approved despite published animal and human anecdotal evidence that they are helpful across a broad range of conditions. Whereas two exosome artificial products were quickly approved, and more are coming for other applications, the business and intellectual property landscape for using naturally occurring homologous exosomes is unclear.

Chapter 11

ANIMAL STUDIES

It is not the strongest of the species that survives, nor the most intelligent, but the one most responsive to change.

—Charles Darwin

I have good news! I believe that the remainder of this book should be more interesting to you because people love stories and especially stories with happy endings. The first half of the book was the investment you and I made to understand how exosomes are a new paradigm and the minimal basic knowledge to understand cell biology, aging, regenerative medicine, immunology, and the FDA. Now, we will embark on the published science, and in subsequent chapters, I will share my anecdotal experiences from over 1800 actual injections of MSC exosomes in patients.

When testing a new product, many times researchers use animal models. There are both good and bad aspects to this. On the one hand, much of human experience turns on the relative superiority of the value of human life over other species. A future version of humanity, with fewer farm animals and one that has outgrown the need to consume other sentient animals, may judge us poorly for that, but that is the current state of affairs with regard to "humane" treatment of animals.

Whether you believe in evolution or not, most people don't subscribe to racist eugenics openly, so the testing on humans is rightly, quite limited. As we get closer to the supposed family tree, people get more squeamish. In other words, sacrificing a mouse to look at their organs at autopsy is less repugnant than sacrificing a chimpanzee.

One nice thing about evolutionary theory is its strong correlation to genetics. That is partly because the morphology that defines differences in evolutionary branches often correlates nearly perfectly with genetic divergences. If we have certain genes, they are conserved, and so in most cases, a mammal, like a mouse, shares nearly 97.5% of the exact same genes, according to the Korea Mouse Phenotyping Center. The nearer they are to humans on the evolutionary tree, the fewer minor differences there will be; these are commonly known as SNP (single nucleotide polymorphisms) within a gene, although they can be more than just one base pair difference. SNPs also occur within the human family but as evolutionary theory goes, the farther a species is from humans, the more significant differences there are in the non-coding DNA. That said, the differences in functional genes (coding DNA) are generally minimal since humans and mice share an ancestor "only" 80 million years ago.

So what? So, the reasons that many of the studies we will discuss used human MSC exosomes to treat animal subjects are explained above. We already have access to human MSCs and their exosomes, and we find sacrificing lab animals in experiments to be morally more acceptable than sacrificing humans. When we start describing the types of experiments that have been done, you will understand what I mean.

There are hundreds of published studies using Human MSC exosomes to treat animal models of disease. Keep in mind that they often fall into the trap of needing to suggest one or two molecules are accounting for the benefits. They never list all the notes in the symphonies that the exosomes contain because there are simply too many to name, and they can vary. Academics work to publish, not bring products to market.

PREMATURE BIRTH INJURY

Harvard professor and stem cell researcher Dr. Stella Kourembanas, has been studying problems of premature birth. There are many problems including blindness from retinal damage, infectious complications, brain hemorrhage, and lung disease from incomplete development of the lungs and their ability to stay open with a chemical surfactant.

Kourembanas did experiments with a chemically induced form of lung fibrosis and showed that the group of mice treated with MSC exosomes had their fibrosis effectively prevented or reversed on autopsy.[1] In another experiment, she gave only one group of newborn mice MSC exosomes on day 4 after birth and exposed both groups to 75% concentration of oxygen. The group given exosomes had much less bronchopulmonary dysplasia at autopsy on day 14 compared to the untreated group.[2]

Since 2012, she has conducted numerous experiments with stem cells and prematurity but eventually she concluded that only the MSC exosomes, not the stem cells, were needed. She then compiled the results of MSC exosomes for all diseases of prematurity into a 2022 paper entitled "[MSC exosomes] and Perinatal Injury: One Formula for Many Diseases"[3]

Korean researchers also showed that in the case of intra-ventricular hemorrhage in newborn rats, the protective effect of MSC exosomes was largely mediated via BDNF (brain-derived neurotrophic factor) in the exosomes and that those exosomes alone were as effective as MSCs.[4]

In another world, these findings of improvement for common, serious, and difficult to mitigate conditions should warrant immediate trials of MSC exosomes in human babies with prematurity. Unfortunately, if there is no money to be gained from developing a therapy that can't be owned, who is going to pay for this? Let me put it this way. If you decided that doing daily deep breathing exercises and meditation, followed by ten pushups and twenty sit-ups a day could lower your risk of some health condition, would you invest your money to develop this as your patented secret treatment? Who is going to pay you for something that anyone can copy?

Since the FDA may not have the legal authority or desire to award a company with exclusive rights to a ubiquitous natural healing modality like exosomes, there is no driving force outside of academia to even investigate mitigating human diseases of prematurity with something proven to work in lab animals. If you wanted to use money from philanthropies, you might get academic trials proving efficacy, but then the issue would be which exosome company to use given that none of them have specific FDA-approval for treating prematurity. If only the taxpayer money could be spent to fund researchers who worked for a tax-payer-owned exosome companies that could gain FDA approval! Sadly, the naïve question that I get from many patients, "If this works, why doesn't the FDA or drug companies approve it?" doesn't take into consideration what motivates those entities.

STROKE RECOVERY

Why did the premature mice treated with exosomes do better than the untreated control group? Simply put, the body is designed to heal with a combination of reduced inflammation, new blood vessel creation, stem cell migration and copying, de-differentiation, and repair. So, if the brain damage from prematurity was decreased by adding more exosomes than those that are normally secreted by inflammation and stem cells, would the same benefit occur with an older brain?

To test this, Liu et al. looked at what would happen with an artificial stroke model. They closed off the middle cerebral artery of mice and gave one-half of the mice MSC exosomes while leaving the other group untreated. They found that the treated group had less brain damage, but that benefit was lessened if they blocked two mRNA: IL-33 and ST2.[5]

Sorry to repeat myself here, but this result alone would justify immediate testing and approval for human use to mitigate suffering, disability, and death from strokes. But since no one would want to take the financial and legal risk to do this trial, knowing it is unclear how they could monetize and protect their "invention," process, or product, who is going to lead the way?

MYOCARDIAL INFARCTION

One of the main reasons people die is heart attacks. Both heart attacks and strokes fall under the category of atherosclerotic disease. This type of disease is generally known as "hardening of the arteries," and it represents the natural final common pathway our vessels. Basically, arteries have elastic collagen that, like the old tires on a car, get less rubbery with time from oxidation and biochemical degradation. Less stretchy arteries produce less "bounce back" or *Windkessel* effect (explained in Chapter 13). Think of it like a fresh tubular balloon versus an old one. If the balloon stretches out, it will stretch back. If it is brittle, it will stretch less, and more force is required in the form of pressure because the balloon won't spring back as well. Higher blood pressures are therefore the *result* of atherosclerosis, but the increased turbulent flow causes more damage and hardening of the arteries as well.

Sometimes, in arteries where there are deposited atherosclerotic plaques, the turbulent flow and increased pressure in the artery will rupture the internal lining of the vessel. That causes a blood clot to form to stop the damage in the artery. That **thromboembolic** (blood clot inside a vessel) clot can block the flow of arterial blood downstream, resulting in a myocardial infarction in the heart or a stroke in the case of arteries to the brain. If the clot can't be removed with blood thinners or an emergency stent (small tube), there is a high risk of permanent damage.

To study the effects of MSC exosomes on myocardial infarction, there have been many studies proving the benefits in animal models. Zheng et al. performed a meta-analysis (pooling of different studies) and found statistically significant benefits from ten combined experiments. Specifically, the ejection fraction, which is the percent of blood ejected versus the total available to be ejected, was 3.67% better. The infarct size was 4.52% smaller. The fibrosis area (scar) was 7.04% smaller. And the apoptosis rate was 8.23% less.[6]

More cardiac function after a heart attack means that the metabolic, electrical, and muscular ability of the heart was much improved if the test animals received the abnormally high numbers of exosomes over what the body would normally muster from being injured, inflamed, and then recruiting its own available stem cells with their own available exosome numbers and potency.

What is the take-home lesson? If you are at 100% of your exosome secretion capacity, you may still end up with permanent and serious deficits from heart muscle death and scarring. If you take an abnormally high number of exosomes at the time of your injury, your ability to mitigate the damage also will be abnormally high, and your serious long-term damages may be lessened as long as the animal studies translate into humans.

Once again, if this were a world run by logic and good intentions, someone should study this in humans to prevent morbidity and mortality from heart attacks. But since we live in a world run by money, fatalism, and risk aversion, this study may never happen at all.

DAMAGE CAUSES AGING OF JOINTS

The title of this section might seem confusing to you until you think deeply about what we said about aging. Remember when I told you that stem cells were immortal, but they need a little time between cell divisions to restore their telomeres? When you damage a joint surface, the call to heal may be too unrelenting to give those cartilage stem cells the time to regrow telomeres. The result is that injury makes even a youngster's cartilage-producing chondrocytes overworked and literally age faster. There have been dozens of studies proving the efficacy of MSC exosomes in animal models of arthritis.[7]

To investigate the effects of MSC exosomes on intentional joint damage, Jin et al. surgically removed the medial knee menisci and transected anterior cruciate ligaments of mice. They injected the knees of the experimental animals with either human MSCs or MSC exosomes weekly until they sacrificed the animals at eight weeks. Can you guess what happened? The mice that received either MSCs or just exosomes had less arthritis damage and more collagen regeneration at autopsy.[8]

The most interesting part of this story isn't that the mice healed better because if it did that for hearts and then brains, how hard would it be to repair a knee? What is most interesting is that the knees that were damaged and healed naturally showed higher percentages of senescent cells in the cartilage. However, the knees that healed in the presence of extra exosomes had fewer senescent cells as measured by **B-galactosidase**. Whether it be from increased numbers, quality, or performance of the stem cells, the suggestion is that abnormally effective healing from MSC exosomes works in such a manner that leaves the joint surfaces less "old" and therefore prone to less arthrosis (burned-out and thinned joint surfaces).

So, who is going to fund the study to prove that MSC exosomes can reverse joint damage, given that this is strongly suggested by the animal studies? Will it be groups of orthopedic surgeons? Not likely. Will it be rheumatologists? Perhaps. But will it be the National Institute of Health or any drug company? Not likely since the intellectual property path forward would be mirky at best for them.

OF MICE AND MEN

You might be mad if you are understanding the research presented in this chapter. But to whom should you direct your anger? Human nature? The legal system? The concept of property and ownership itself?

Mother nature has provided us with a tool kit to make 100% of the exosomes you can make with your current state of health, stemness, and epigenetic programming. She has also made scientists who can and do manage to produce pure, potent, and biologically active exosomes for sale.

The problem is that there are few medical practitioners who, outside of their own families, feel inclined to learn and adapt to this new paradigm of supranormal exosome usage to accelerate repair. Your body, when faced with the prospect of joint damage, heart attack, or stroke, uses an FDA-unapproved method to repair, just like every other closely related animal. You have the ability to find someone to give you more of the same thing that is working but in higher numbers and with better, youthful potency.

So, what happens when we follow science, intuition, and experience to mitigate incompletely treated injuries that stopped repairing long ago? Well, the next few chapters, filled with anecdotes from actual patients of mine, will begin to answer those questions and, in doing so, present some interesting prospects for a better future of health, wellness, and longevity.

Chapter 12

ANECDOTES IN MSK PROBLEMS

The art of healing comes from nature,
not from the physician.
Therefore the physician must start from nature,
with an open mind.

—Paracelsus (Renaissance physician)

If you have a body and you live long enough, you will develop MSK problems. It's as inevitable as needing to go to the auto repair shop if you put 300,000 miles on your vehicle. Of course, if we have plentiful exosomes from copious stem cells, like a fetus or an invertebrate in the ocean, different rules of regeneration might apply. But for now, you ache because of incompletely repaired stuff everywhere, and maybe the MSC exosomes can help mitigate that as they did in the lab mice and in the patients that I will be presenting.

Just so we are all on the same page, let's take a moment to define some important terms of the musculoskeletal system which are the structures that form the shape, posture, and load-bearing functions of the body.

"THE LEG BONE'S CONNECTED TO THE...SHIN BONE"

We have roughly 206 bilaterally symmetrical **BONES** that, when they connect to other bones, do so at what are known as **JOINTS**. Many joints have watertight fibrous capsules that allow the joint fluid inside to lubricate the movements. Inside these joints, we have slippery and hard collagen, much like Teflon, which is the renewable lining called hyaline **CARTILAGE** that covers the contacting surfaces of the bones. This cartilage is produced by the ends of the bones themselves. When doctors and especially radiologists describe damage in the joints, they usually call it "arthritis" instead of what it truly is, which is arthrosis. That is because the assumption is that all older people, with wear and damage, are all getting the same thing, and our language is a bit lazy.

Sure, there are true **arthritides** (pronounced: ar-THRI-ti-deez, the plural of arthritis) that can happen from acute infection, autoimmune problems, and chemical imbalances like gout and pseudogout, but in general, clinicians assume you have what the vast majority of others come in with, and not one of those exotic problems. Unless the doctor writes some relevant history in the radiographic submission that would suggest otherwise (e.g., acute trauma, fevers, or inflammatory white blood cells and crystals from a joint aspiration), the radiologist will just call it osteoarthritis although sometimes they may call it arthrosis.

Although it may end up as bone wearing on the bone, arthritis begins as thinning cartilage wearing down on the thinning cartilage, like two old brake pads. The creation of fresh joint cartilage is accomplished by stem cells known as chondrocytes, which are mesengenically transformed from MSCs, but they are also stimulated by MSC exosomes, as we learned from the mice experiments in the last chapter. Arthrosis (aka osteoarthritis) is a clinical syndrome that encompasses specific changes like thinning of the joint cartilage, osteophytes (aka bone spurs), and changes in the subchondral bone, such as cysts and hardening. Osteoarthritis likely represents the burning out, without adequate replacement, of viable stem cells that maintain the bones and other cartilage of the joint. If poor alignment, trauma, aging, and inflammation are significant, then the ligaments and cushioning cartilage that support the joints can also become damaged along with the joint surfaces.

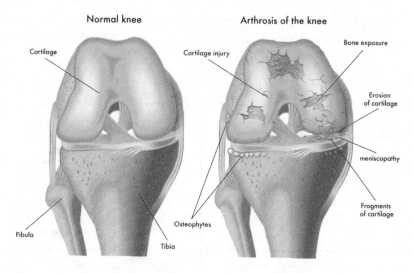

Normal knee

Arthrosis of the knee

Cartilage

Cartilage injury

Bone exposure

Erosion of cartilage

meniscopathy

Fragments of cartilage

Fibula

Osteophytes

Tibia

12.1: Knee Arthrosis (aka arthritis)

EDGE LINING CARTILAGE TO SEAT YOUR JOINTS PROPERLY

Remember that joints are where bones move against each other. Larger joints, like the shoulders, hips, and knees, have specialized edge-liners called **labra** or **menisci** (singular: labrum and meniscus). These hard and yet flexible structures, like the plastic liners of the old metal bottle caps, serve to keep bones in alignment and therefore slow down the lifetime of friction that leads to arthritis. In the shoulders and hips, we call those liners labra; in the knees only, they are known as menisci. Acute force, especially in an arthritic joint, can cause labral and meniscal tears, which can be easily resected like hangnails and some-times even surgically sutured back together or reattached to the bone. Unfortunately, these fibroelastic structures are poorly vascularized, and therefore, surgeons often recom-mend resection rather than repair, leaving a setup for more arthritis from increased friction in the future.

Common injuries to the shoulder causing labral tears include falling on an outstretched arm and shoulder dislo-cation. Hip labral tears are common with sports, falls, and when the joint is arthritic. Knee meniscal tears are com-mon from skiing, contact sports, and from any rotation with a weight-bearing stationary foot.

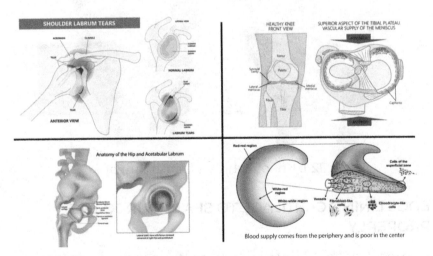

12.2: Labra and Menisci cushion and seat the bones of the larger joints[1]

While bones connect at joints, bones are also fastened together by **LIGAMENTS**. There are many ligaments around the ankles, wrists, shoulders, knees, and spinal vertebrae and they also form watertight joint capsules mentioned above. The ligaments are maintained by rare, collagen-producing stem cells called tenocytes, which are specialized MSCs that have undergone the MESENGENIC transformation shown before in Chapter 4. Whatever you call the stem cells that are producing ligaments and tendons, it is clear that they are stem cells and they probably originate from those magical MSCs.

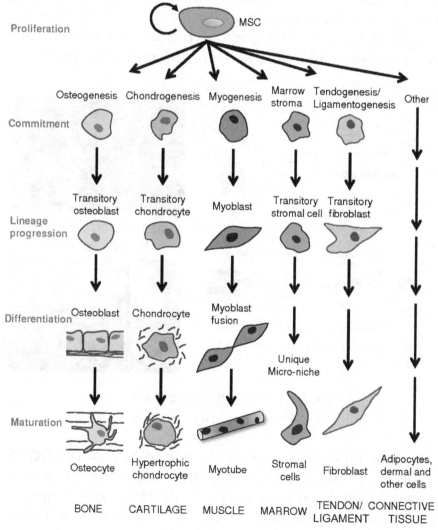

12.3: Mesengenic Transformation

Like a cable in a suspension bridge, ligaments and tendons are made up of collagen fibrils, bundled into fibers, and then bundled into fascicles. This configuration gives redundant strength and elasticity to both bridges and the hard-working tissues of our MSK system. The tenocytes, derived from MSCs, lay down the collagen and extracellular matrix to rebuild new strength while the remaining fiber bundles keep the structure from failing. The figure below, adapted from Asahara et al.'s *"Tendons and Ligaments: Connecting Developmental Biology to MSK Disease Pathogenesis,"* describes some of the possible triggers for this mesengenic differentiation and repair of ligaments and tendons.[2]

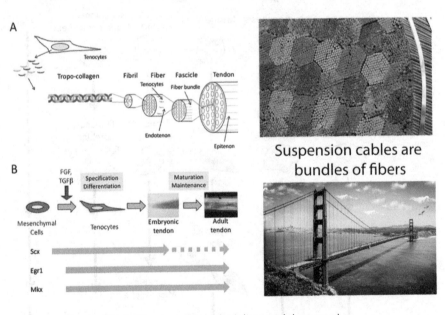

Suspension cables are bundles of fibers

12.4: Suspension bridge cables and tendons/ligaments are similar

Whereas ligaments connect bones to bones, **TENDONS** connect muscles to bones. Other than that, they are essentially the same as ligaments and the same tenocyte stem cells, derived from MSCs and then differentiated by the mesengenic process, are also under the influence of MSC exosome signaling. The only technical difference when you get a dysfunction of a tendon is we call it a "Strain" (with a T, like in tendon), whereas we call a ligament injury a "Sprain" (with a P, like a sprained ankle). If a tendon is strained but incompletely healed over time, it will still function like a suspension cable with some torn fibers, but you may see holes or calcification on an ultrasound or MRI consistent with TENDINOSIS (also spelled tendonosis).

BUT WAIT, THERE'S MORE

This catchphrase from infomercials would seem to apply here. So you know about the bones, the joints, the labra/menisci, ligaments, and tendons; what else could there be? For completeness' sake, we should also mention a few other groups that can also play the MSK blues. There are about 160 **BURSAS** (or bursae, plural of bursa) in your body; they are remarkable fluid-filled gel bags that cushion the movements of muscles and tendons. For example, in some runners or cyclists, the bursas lining the outside of the femoral bumps can become inflamed by rubbing of the gluteal muscles or the iliotibial band, causing trochanteric bursitis. Treatment is rest and steroids, but the anti-inflammatory exosomes could also be helpful.

AND EVEN MORE

So, dwindling numbers and quality of stem cells in all those aforementioned components of the MSK system can lead to pain and loss of function via arthrosis, tendinosis, and ligamentosis (an uncommonly used term), but let's not forget **osteoporosis** leading to fractures, tears in cartilage, tears in ligaments, and muscles that can even detach at the site of their bone insertions (an **avulsion**). An old system is a brittle system in both its stem cell exhaustion and mechanical resilience.

With time and accretive damage, we can be sure there is incidental inflammation and senescence happening as well. Old tissues get injured, which brings in inflammation, which recruits stem cells, which produce exosomes at whatever 100% capacity looks like, and then the local osteoblasts, chondrocytes, or tenocytes try to copy their way out of the damage. They do an admirable job, but like any "immortal" stem cell, even in a fresh new stem cell flask, they will eventually acquire errors, shortened telomeres, epigenetic gene silencing, senescence, and then apoptosis (programmed cell death).

Even under ideal conditions, the MSK system can break down because of other factors such as alignment or conformation of the body, poor posture from inadequate core strength, poor balance of muscular to tendon strength, weak ligaments, loss of adequate blood flow, loss of nervous system function, inadequate nutrition, and even genetic disorders (mostly of collagen synthesis). If you are enjoying a life without pain or limitation of activity, you are doing something right or you might be too young to have acquired enough damage.

TESTING ON MYSELF

As I mentioned in Chapter 3, I knew about exosomes, but after hearing the neurologist with the motorcycle crash story just four weeks before, I was willing to try them on myself. Years earlier, I had maniacally practiced a repetitive golf swing, and afterward, my knee was in pain with twisting and flexion. The usual treatment for a torn meniscus is surgery, but I just took my telomerase activator, and it was bearable for years. Nevertheless, it did have some clicking and occasional pain, suggesting that the meniscus never completely healed. After meeting the purveyors of the MSC exosome company, I ordered my own samples and injected my own knee joint. Within weeks and now over four years later, the knee has no longer hurt nor clicked. Placebo effect? Attribution bias? I don't really care as long as it doesn't hurt or click.

Similarly, I had suffered years of a sore right Achilles tendon and a painful right rotator cuff tendon (the subscapularis). Exosome injections into those areas resolved the pain for at least a year and a half. That said, my continued yoga and swimming meant that I've had to inject those areas twice more to keep the pain and loss of function away.

Think of it like a brake pad. If you are able to regrow the structures from 40% to 60%, you may not have symptoms, but it is still not 100%, and continued injury resulting in tendinosis will accrue. It's not "use it or lose it" but rather "use it, and you will lose it" when it comes to most collagen-based tissues like joint surfaces, tendons, and ligaments. Unlike muscles, which have satellite stem cells that copy and cause muscle hypertrophy when damaged by resistance, most of the musculoskeletal system wears down with use and time. Think of the lint trap in a clothes dryer; there is always something in there, so that means your sheets and clothes are losing some integrity, right?

After having good results with my own treatments, I began to cautiously offer treatment to my family and friends. To this day, my siblings and their families have never tried exosomes. But my mom has become a true believer with over 34 injections to date.

DOUG, THE RUNNER

One of my favorite patients, Doug, was willing to try a knee injection for his osteoarthritis. It was markedly better, and he could resume his running passion. An engineer, inventor, and my occasional sci-fi movie buddy, he allowed me to inject his knee. Keep in mind that Doug likes to hike up mountains and run the number of miles in each Julian year. I suppose it's a good thing that he isn't following a Jewish or Chinese dating system. Now at 84 years old, he remains active running and although we couldn't stave off a partial knee replacement on one side, he continues to enjoy running over 2023 miles a year, up and down the mountains of Southern California. If exosomes had been covered by insurance, I'm fairly certain he would have done multiple injections and may have even avoided the knee surgery. Also, the costs would have been less to the healthcare system than paying for a knee surgery.[3]

RUNNING UP THAT HILL

I have a friend, RA, a 63-yo martial artist, whom I first met in Hawaii. He had already paid a deposit for an allogeneic stem cell treatment, so he decided to do a sort of A/B experiment with one side receiving stem cells and the other receiving exosomes. In his case, the stem cell-treated knee remained problematic, but the exosome-treated knee became pain-free. Keep in mind that this person runs up 30-degree hills, leg presses 1000 lbs, and kicks a heavy bag for martial arts. Interestingly, despite the resolution of all pain and limitations after two knee injections, he wanted to improve his "brake pads" as much as possible. Instead of stopping at two injections, he took a total of 7 exosome shots on each side. Sure, the fact that I provided the shots to my friend at cost helped, but I was impressed by his commitment to the idea of going beyond just asymptomatic to something closer to youthful functioning.

NO MORE ICE, EXCEPT IN THE APRES SKI COCKTAILS

One of my friends and golf buddies, CY, is a 56-year-old man with a vacation home in Deer Valley, Utah. An avid skier, he became accustomed to icing his swollen knees after each day's alpine adventure. He spent most of his early 50s being treated with hyaluronic acid knee injections, which helped with some pain but are not intended to cure osteoarthritis. About four years ago, he was one of the first people to allow me to treat him, and ever since then, he gets an annual "tune-up". Why? Because since doing the injections, he has never had to ice his knees again; they no longer hurt after skiing, and he enjoys nearly thirty days a year doing what he loves.

TRUSTING THE EXPERTS

In contrast, I had a 73-year-old, tall, and active man come to me for knee injections twice. He stated the first and second exosome injections resulted in less knee pain but that he was still considering knee replacements. Interestingly, when we compared the plain film X-rays of his knees from before and months after the shots, the black space indicating the cartilage had visibly grown. Instead of repeating therapy with exosomes, his orthopedic surgeon recommended not repeating X-rays and proceeding with the surgeries. Thankfully, he did fine after knee replacements, but it should be noted that up to 20% of people have more pain after total knee replacement.[4] Was there a missed opportunity to help repair his knees without surgery? Perhaps, but we will never know.

HALF FULL, OR HALF EMPTY

One of the most instructive patients was one of my earliest, BH, a 49-year-old airline pilot with a torn rotator cuff. I gave him a shoulder injection and after a month, he felt 50% better. Whereas I was apologetic, he replied, "what for? We just need to do it again." So, he returned, and we repeated the injection. By another month, he was 100% and has remained fine in his rotator cuff tendinosis injury. As a result of treating him, I always adjust patients' expectations, stating, "If it stays the same or gets worse, don't repeat. If it gets better, consider repeating after a few months. And if you are pain-free, don't repeat." Although, if the martial artist and my skier friend are any indication, getting ahead of the curve and maintenance are not a bad idea.

EARLY VERSUS LATE COLLAGEN

I learned another important lesson from an actor friend, VS, who was 56 at the time of his knee arthritis treatment. Just a few weeks after his knee treatment, the chronic knee pain had largely resolved. Feeling great, he played beach volleyball for two hours and ended up having worse pain and likely creating new tears in the joint cartilage. Another case was 54-year-old AL, whose 3-year rotator cuff pain went away after injection. He felt so good that he excessively bench pressed in the first week and injured the other shoulder. When I think about the timing, type three, early, and disorganized collagen is not as strong as remodeled, type one, permanent collagen. Since those experiences, I always recommend at least 6-8 weeks of lighter activity, even and *especially* if you feel no pain since the new collagen is like wet cement and is more easily injured.

MISCELLANEOUS TENDONS AND LIGAMENTS

Because the aging, damage, and incomplete repair of tendons and ligaments is a ubiquitous problem for all of us, I have had the opportunity to treat many of these areas. I don't charge more for multiple procedures, so if the patient has purchased enough product, we will do many shots into various areas. The patient will point to where it hurts, and I'll mark it. As long as there is no dangerous anatomy nearby, we can easily inject it, and in the majority of cases, the pain resolves within a month or so. Why? Because the MSC exosomes signal local stem cells to rebuild the structures. That's how Mother Nature designed the system;

despite being unapproved and not standard of care, your body tried and failed to repair it with 100% of exosomes. If you introduce new inflammation with PRP, it will bring in new stem cells, which will secrete new exosomes. Or you could simply insert the exosomes and skip to the regenerative signals without the exogenous inflammation and stem cell recruitment.

In conclusion, there certainly are cases where patients have experienced little to no improvement. I even had one patient develop a serious knee infection, which, in fairness, can happen with any joint injection with steroids or hyaluronic acid, for example. Nevertheless, after over 1800 injections, the majority of which were MSK-related, I can estimate that the response rate is around 70% and that MSK indications represent some of the "low-hanging fruit" of exosome therapy.

If you think about the chart with the mesengenic process of differentiation and note that the cells that make up the stem cells of the bones, muscles, tendons, ligaments, and cartilage all arise from MSCs, it makes you wonder how much of the system of stem cell regulation, deployment, and reactivation via exosome signaling we truly understand.

Chapter 13

ANECDOTES IN CARDIOVASCULAR TREATMENTS

A man is as old as his arteries.

—Thomas Sydenham (17th century English physician)

It is wrong to consider the cardiovascular system as its own entity, but we will do so anyway. I say that because there are hormonal and neurological aspects to maintaining blood pressure which we will explore.

In real time, the maintenance of blood pressure to perfuse your brain and kidneys is a top priority to stay alive and conscious. Instead of thinking about a passive plumbing system that carries oxygenated blood away from the heart and deoxygenated blood back to the heart, there are instantaneous interactions between your blood pressure sensors in the aorta and neck arteries, which feed back and control your sympathetic "fight or flight" output. This output tells your body how much "tightness" you require in your arteries (like kinking a garden hose to make a stream go farther) and how much work your heart needs to produce in terms of heart rate and force.

AFFERENT means from body to the central nervous system; these are the sensing pathways shown in blue (see Figure

13.1). In the aortic arch, you have pressure sensors that travel via the afferent Vagus nerve (Cranial nerve X, "10") back to the medulla in the brainstem. In the neck arteries, you have pressure and O2/CO2 sensors that travel back to the medulla via the afferent Glossopharyngeal nerve (Cranial nerve IX, "9").

In response, the medulla coordinates EFFERENT commands from the CNS out to the periphery; they are either parasympathetic vagal (relaxing) or sympathetic (exciting) commands. The green lines in the cartoon show sympathetic commands going to the arteries, heart muscle, and cardiac pacemakers via the sympathetic nerves. They also show the relaxing vagal nerve stimulation to the pacemakers in light green.

Baroreceptors and chemoreceptors

AFFERENT   EFFERENT

Solitary nucleus

Medulla

IX: Glossopharyngeal nerve

X: Vagus nerve

Spinal cord

Sympathetic chain

Parasympathetic vagus nerve

Carotid sinus baroreceptor

Carotid body chemoreceptor

Sympathetic nerves

Aortic chemoreceptor

Aortic baroreceptor

SA node

AV node

Blood vessels

13.1: Pressure and chemical sensors regulate BP via brainstem reflexes

So, what I'm saying is that maintaining adequate blood pressure isn't something that you can just "get around to doing" like digestion or even balancing your blood glucose. It is a critically important real-time function, just like breathing. When the pressure receptors send an improper signal, you can faint because the feedback is so immediate; that is called a vasovagal syncopal episode. At least you're not a giraffe! When it bends down to drink, the blood pressure doubles to 480/320 and yet it doesn't have a stroke.

There are also hormones that serve to maintain blood pressure. **Aldosterone** from the adrenal glands and **anti-diuretic hormone (ADH)** from the pituitary gland in the brain change your fluid balance by retaining or excreting electrolytes and water. Finally, **angiotensin II** enhances production of aldosterone and ADH, and it also controls the vascular tone directly by increasing sympathetic activity. It is made with the cooperation of the liver, kidneys, and lung.

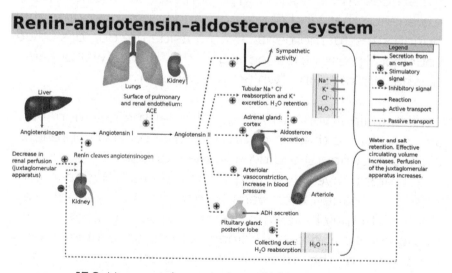

Renin-angiotensin-aldosterone system

13.2: Hormonal regulation of blood pressure[1]

Right before I started writing this, I was on the phone with a lovely 69-yo man who, for years now, has taken a telomerase activator. He takes no medications and exercises actively, without pain, by running, karate, calisthenics, and weight training. Remember the last chapter when we said everyone has something that hurts? Well, for the last five years, this man has been taking the telomerase activator that I've been taking for 16 years, and he seems to be doing pretty well, all things considered.

He was concerned about something we call "white coat hypertension," which raises a very interesting question. Should he be concerned? The following explanation is going to be difficult for most of you, and especially you doctors, to understand, but what you call "white coat hypertension" isn't a psychological condition. It simply reflects the aging of the arterial system. Typically, a person says they have this condition when they find a blood pressure check in the doctor's office shows numbers like 180/110 whereas in the comfort of their home, it can be 120/60. Are they the same person? What does it mean? A young person, exposed to stress, won't experience that kind of change, and you can assume that during stressful moments, even outside the doctor's office, your blood pressure is shooting up that high as well because of what you're calling "white coat hypertension."

I will explain it very simply, but first let me mention what Jim said to me that I thought was spot on and yet reflects a deep misunderstanding that everyone shares: "I suspect that I might have hardening of the arteries." I had to inform him that hearing that was like hearing a 69-year-old say, "I suspect I may have wrinkles on my face." Unless you are doing something extraordinary, of course, everyone gets hardening of the arteries! The connective tissue of the arteries, like the connective tissue of the skin, loses elasticity from the cross-linking of collagen and the loss of elastin (a protein of the extracellular matrix). If you think about a rubber animal balloon that is fresh from the factory versus one that has been in the cupboard for 70 years, what do you expect the older balloon to do when you inflate it? Well, it won't be as stretchy, and it might even crack, right?

WINDKESSEL (air chamber) EFFECT

The key concept that few people know about, which is why they don't talk about it, is the *Windkessel* effect, which is German for the "wind chamber." The heart pumps out in **systole** (pronounced "SIS-tuh-lee", which is the first "lub" phase before the longer "dub" **diastole** (pronounced dai-ASS-tuh-lee) heart-filling phase. In the pumping systole phase, the arteries are supposed to stretch a bit, storing potential stretchy energy. When the heart and arteries are resting in diastole, that stretchy energy recoils to push blood forward, evening out the flow over the cardiac cycle. In your body, the large arteries are stretchy when you're young, so you can maintain pressure to the receptors more easily. As those balloons start to become hardened, like lead pipes, the bounce back of the *Windkessel* effect is lost, and so in order to maintain adequate blood pressure, you need to increase your sympathetic tone (flight or fight response).[2]

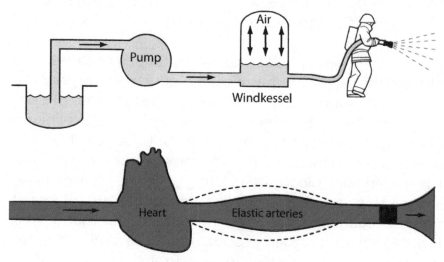

13.3: *Windkessel* effect

Why hasn't anyone mentioned this? It's a combination of ignorance and just following dogma. Of course, doctors know arteries get harder, but dogma tells us to consider high blood pressure to be a **disease** that must be treated by blocking the sympathetic response or lowering blood volume. They don't understand that high blood pressure is a normal **adaptation** to having stiff arteries from so-called aging. This is <u>not to say that high blood pressure isn't dangerous or shouldn't be treated</u>. Over time, high blood pressure and the turbulent flow inside arteries increase atherosclerosis as well as the risk of strokes, heart attacks, and end-organ damage to things like kidneys and eyes.

You may ask, "Is there any evidence for this new theory of yours, Dr. Park?" Well, is there evidence that people in their 80s might have more wrinkles on their faces than people in their 20s? That said, every single table of normal blood pressures as people age shows this trend, but more importantly, the **PULSE PRESSURE** always increases proportionally with aging. The difference between the pressure during systole (the top number) and pressure during diastole (the bottom number) is called the pulse pressure. 120/80 translates into 120 minus 80, or a pulse pressure of 40mmHg (millimeters of mercury in a standardized column.)

I'm not even going to bother with citations because they all state the same thing: as we get older, the pulse pressure increases. I submit that this is mainly due to loss of elasticity (and its *Windkessel* effect) mainly from cross-linking of collagen and elastin degradation, but also possibly from age-related changes in the muscles of the arteries and the endothelial (blood vessel lining) cells themselves. I also submit that just as wrinkles likely occur because of loss of normal collagen, damage to the extracellular matrix, and the degradation of skin-producing cells, a similar age-related process is happening in your arteries.

One final note about pulse pressure. In the early years of testing people's pulse wave analysis (PWA), I would usually find improvements in the pulse pressure after months of taking TA-65. What does that signify? Perhaps the aging of the arteries was somewhat reversed by telomerase activation. I know that after 16 years of taking telomerase activators, I went from 210 lbs and 160/100 to 185lbs and 130/85, and I still don't have hypertension (or reading glasses) at age 56.

Is there any evidence to support my theory? Nzietcheung et al in 2011 published a study looking at the telomeres in the blood vessel cells of aortas with atherosclerosis versus without. They found that the large arteries with atherosclerosis had shorter telomeres.[3] I suggest that excess turbulence causes damage that must be responded to with stem cell replication, just as in a runner's knee or an alcoholic's liver. More trauma means more replication and shortened telomeres. The turbulence is causing both the mechanical injury to permit atherosclerosis and the cellular aging of the blood vessels.

LYMPHATIC SYSTEM

For completeness, we should also discuss the lymphatic system, which collects fluid that is no longer in the blood vessels but rather in the tissues themselves. The lymphatic drainage empties into the venous system near the left collarbone. This drainage also allows for regional isolation and immune responses, as described in Chapter 9. If you get cancer in your leg, your groin lymph nodes on that side might swell up. If you get a tooth infection, the lymph nodes in your neck might swell up. If your lymphatic system is clogged with parasitic worms, you can have elephantiasis of that leg.

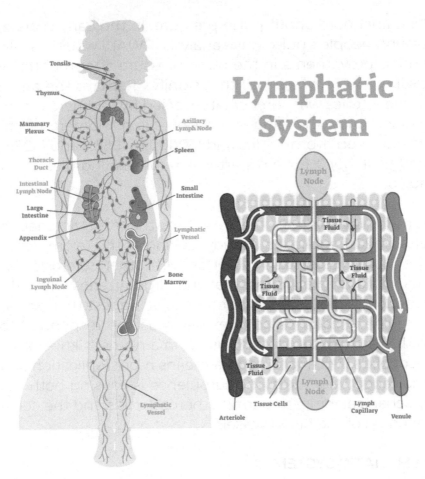

13.4: Lymphatic System

ARTERIES AND VEINS

Except with blood going to and from the lungs, the anatomical drawings show arteries as red and the veins as blue. That is because the blood heading away from the heart is literally redder (more oxygenated), and when it returns to the heart, it is more blue (deoxygenated). All tissues require oxygen, glucose, ATP (an energy molecule), and they need to clear CO_2 and other waste products. As shown below, the arterial system connects to the venous system in the capillaries. Another important distinction is that veins have less muscle (so they don't create that pulse you can feel), but they do have one-way valves to prevent backflow and promote return to the heart.

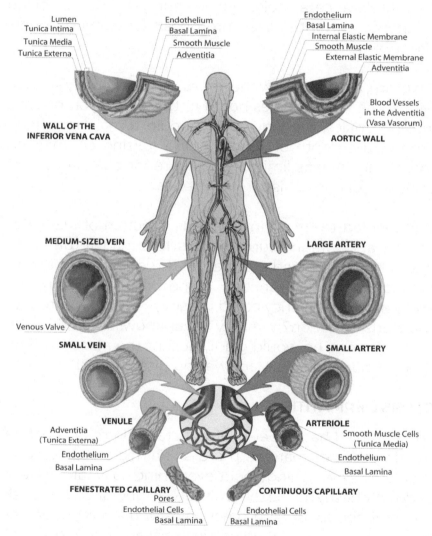

13.5: Arteries and Veins

VENOUS INSUFFICIENCY

When I was living in Hawaii for a year, I was introduced to a man who was an 84-year-old with extreme leg swelling. He had a history of strokes at age 42, and then, at age 81, he fell and had an epidural hematoma. To control his blood pressure, he was taking an angiotensin receptor blocker and a sympathetic blocker. He was also taking two pills for glucose intolerance, a cholesterol-lowering drug, and a blood thinner to prevent further thrombosis (or clotting) events like stroke.

On exam, his legs below the knees were extremely swollen with some fluid bubbles noted in the skin. If you pressed into his ankles, the indentation would remain for a long time to the depth of your pressing (pitting edema). His mental acuity was limited, and he reportedly had a 90% occlusion of one of his carotid arteries.

We decided to try an intravenous injection of MSC exosomes, and within four days, his legs had returned to normal and remained that way for three years. What combination of cardiac function, blood proteins, lymphatics, and venous sufficiency could possibly have accounted for this transformation? We may never know, but in the case of the patient, he would gladly accept the placebo effect as an explanation if his leg swelling disappeared.[4]

STASIS DERMATITIS

To be frank, I had never heard of stasis dermatitis before treating the next patient. There isn't a doctor in the world that knows everything about everything so what we learn to do is honestly define the limits of our ignorance. If you ask an engineer about fluid mechanics, you wouldn't expect him to help you if he studied electrical engineering, right? But hopefully, he would be able to do a web search and apply critical reasoning skills to help you. Same for doctors.

Remember the 63-year-old martial artist who took seven knee injections despite feeling normal after the second?

JA was his 86-year-old mother. She had a history of mold exposure, which might have done some damage to her veins or lymphatics. When I treated her, she had severe pitting edema of the lower legs, so much so that her feet were both a shade of purple. Interestingly, when circulation is poor, a person can have **STASIS DERMATITIS**, which in her case manifested as red, itchy bumps on the legs but also red patches on her antecubital fossa (insides of the elbows) that we all know from friends and relatives with eczema.

Despite going to dermatologists, who tried topical steroids and tacrolimus (a T-cell inhibitor that shuts down cytokine production), nothing seemed to help. For some reason, one dose of intravenous MSC exosomes caused the leg swelling and the rashes throughout her body to disappear. Years later, they remain gone. Placebo effect? I don't think it matters much to her.[5]

THE CASE OF THE MYSTERIOUS SHEDDING TOENAIL

MB was a 35-year-old active yoga instructor with a toenail on her big toe that would fall out nearly every month. She didn't have trauma or any nail fungus. Her history was notable for a 5-year history of dermatitis on the fingers, which seemed to improve with intravenous MSC exosome treatment three months prior. She was also pleased with the facial rejuvenation microneedling with exosomes that she had received. After injecting near the nail bed and the arteries of the big toe with a very small amount of exosomes, she has not had the nail fall out for three years now! Was the common factor for the dermatitis and the shedding toenail simply suboptimal circulation?

NO MORE COLD FEET

One of the 34 treatments I did for my mother was to treat the arteries leading to her feet. At age 83, she complained of chronically cold feet. I injected MSC exosomes around the two main arteries: the posterior tibial and dorsalis pedis, and for over two years, she has had no further complaints. Two years ago, I got frozen water into my Apres ski boots by stepping into a puddle and when I removed my boots, the feet were both blue, suggesting frostbite. In the months that passed, my feet were always cold, so I decided to inject around my own arteries, and sure enough, I haven't had any problems with excessively cold feet since.

VR was a 31yo man who came to me with chronic numbness, tingling, and loss of touch sensation in both feet from frostbite (age 22), loss of sensation in his left thumb and first two digits from holding a cold object (age 27), and decreased sensation in his right first two digits from a burn (age 30). After each of his three injections, the pain and decreased sensation of the digits improved to the point of being tolerable. Although not fully recovered, the nerve problems and circulation have improved.[6]

BOB, THE BUILDER

At the start of this chapter, I mentioned that the circulatory system is not just pumping blood. We learned that hardening arteries *causes* the adaptation of higher blood pressure. But what we need to understand is that the small vessels are aging and degrading even at the capillary level. That can look like macular degeneration, kidney failure, lumbar disc disease, torn menisci, etc.

In everything, everywhere, and all at once, small vessels are getting old and failing to deliver life's precious blood. The case of Bob illustrates this well, and his recovery could arguably be placed in the next chapter on neurology. You see, all nerves have small blood vessels, and when small blood vessels die, so do those nerves.

Bob was a 75-year-old man who, in his 50s, was a competitive bodybuilder. As you can see below, he looked like Mr. Universe. Five years before, he began to develop progressive neuropathy of both legs. This loss of sensation felt like his feet were wrapped in cellophane, and he couldn't feel light touch. His feet were chronically cold, and he began to lose control of his atrophying calf muscles.

When we met, his previously Greek statue-like calves were emaciated. He couldn't discern light touch or the position of his toes. He also had cold, reddish, dry skin, a 3cm purple patch on his ankle, and needed orthotics to walk his rather unstable gait. What came first, the nerve damage or the vascular insufficiency? Most likely, the small vessel disease (as with diabetic neuropathy from high glucose toxicity) caused the nerve damage, but the nerve damage caused the loss of calf musculature and decreased circulation from lack of demand and pumping action.

What was fascinating was that during the injections of his popliteal arteries and around his sciatic nerves, the leg being treated turned visibly whiter than the untreated leg. Was there some real-time vasoconstriction that was being reversed by signaling the artery or the nerves?

In the following weeks and months, the bodybuilder's body started to rebuild after five years of progressive decline. The second treatment was an ultrasound-guided injection into the popliteal arteries, and again, the sciatic nerves were treated. He now uses no orthotics, the veins on his legs have reappeared, and he has recovered some sensation in his feet. For the first time in years, his calf muscles are responding to voluntary control, and he can walk for a mile on the treadmill without assistive devices like canes. Oh, and the lumbar epidural treatment we did for his back pain resolved that issue.

What is the end of the line for Bob? Maybe this is it. But at least he seems to have improved. The year before our meeting, he had already had a comprehensive evaluation at the Mayo Clinic and was told they couldn't help his idiopathic (unknown cause) nerve damage.[7]

Bob, age 58   Bob, age 75

13.6: Bob, the Builder

VASCULOGENESIS

Vasculogenesis, or angiogenesis, means the creation of new blood vessels. It is a mysterious and yet ubiquitous process. Just as every cell and every capillary in your body is getting older and trying to die, there are forces conspiring to rebuild. During times of stress, such as low oxygen, new vessels can be stimulated to grow. MSCs and their exosomes can promote **VEGF (vascular endothelial growth factor), PDGF (platelet derived growth factor),** and **FGF (fibroblast growth factor),** which are key players in growing new vessels.[8] Since 2000, we have known that there are also circulating specialized stem cells called **EPC (endo-thelial progenitor cells)** that can oversee and physically participate in new vessel growth.[9]

The FDA may say that exosomes from MSCs are not minimally altered and are not being used in a homologous fashion, but there is room for debate since, throughout life, we are constantly using our own MSC exosomes to build new vessels, and to my knowledge, there are no known changes to the naturally produced exosomes after their passive collection.

Chapter 14

ANECDOTES IN NEUROLOGY

The worst part is not in making a mistake
but in trying to justify it,
instead of using it as a heaven-sent warning
of our mindlessness or our ignorance.

—Santiago Ramón y Cajal (Spanish pathologist)

Thanks to Bob's legs coming back to life, we realize that circulation and nerve damage are interrelated. I guarantee that there isn't a person among you who doesn't know someone with foot neuropathy. What if nerve damage, like wrinkles or stiff arteries, is just another emergent property of getting old by stem cell degradation and depletion? Interestingly, being really tall seems to be a risk factor.[1] Better known is the clear relationship between neuropathy and having diabetes, probably by compromising those tiny blood vessels.

Think of your nervous system as a television you purchased back in 1950. Would you really be surprised if a wire burned out or a part of the cathode ray screen was funky? Back in medical school, they filled our young minds with a lot of dogma; to be frank, allopathic medicine is much like a death cult whose core value is "life is a steady march towards decrepitude, and our job is to make the transition just a bit easier without providing false hope."

Does that seem a bit extreme? How much of your health care dollars are spent working with diet, nutrition, mental health, and learning to avoid toxins? Most likely, the points of maximal resource expenditure will occur in cancer treatment and during the bleak last few weeks of your life. If your consciousness or bodily functions leave you earlier, you will simply be parked in an institution until you succumb to another medication error, bed sore, or slip and fall.

Perhaps in neurology, more than any other specialty, the doctor must get comfortable with hopelessness. When I did my medical student rotation at Harlem Hospital in New York City, I knew I could never emotionally survive in a field where the majority of what you do is diagnose the site of a lesion and then provide no probable cure for that problem.

The hopelessness around neurology is deeply rooted in the neuroanatomical studies of Spanish pathologist Santiago Ramón y Cajal. His static observations led to NEURON THEORY, which states neurons are polarized, non-continuous specialized cells that communicate at junctions called synapses; this remains true and meshes well with cell theory.[2] Unfortunately, a corollary to the static observations of the neuron dogma that was passed down to us naïve medical students was the misconception that "you don't make new brain cells." A common trope is estimating the brain cells you kill while engaging in excessive partying. We internalized this dogma despite learning about support cells that reinsulate the nerve cells, macrophage-like mobile immune cells that protect and serve the neurons, and even neural stem cells that create new neurons. In fact, it is now understood that when you sleep, even the oldest and most infirmed of us are making thousands of new neurons in the hippocampus every single night.[3]

NEUROANATOMY FOR BEGINNERS

Just what about nerves makes them so hard to fix? I hate to be bothersome again, but I am now confident that if you have made it this far, you are more than capable of absorbing new concepts. So, before we talk about amazing cases in neurology, let's get to know some basic terms and principles about nerves and the nervous system.

The basic unit of the nervous system is the neuron, and neurons come in many different shapes and specialized functions. A simple description of neurons is that they are polarized electrical relays that communicate at what's called the **synapse**. The sending neuron's electrical charge releases neurotransmitters (like dopamine, for instance) into the synapse, which then binds to the receiving neuron's post-synaptic receptors, initiating a new electrical signal in the neuron at its **dendrite**. That new signal is electrically conducted down a wire called the **axon**, which is insulated by periodic fatty sheaths made of **myelin**. Myelin is made by the supporting **Schwann cells** peripherally and **oligodendrocytes** in the central nervous system. When the electrical impulse reaches the next synapse, a third neuron will continue the relay of the electrical signal or fulfill its function, like recognizing you've heard an F#.

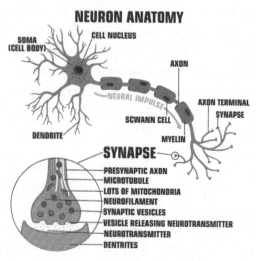

14.1: Neuron structure

NERVOUS SYSTEMS

Mostly, we talk about two nervous systems: the central and the peripheral. The CNS (**central** nervous system) is comprised of the brain and spinal cord, which allow for sensory perceptions, movements, cognition, memory, hormone homeostasis, and painting Renaissance masterpieces.

Then there is the peripheral nervous system, which is just all the nerves that are outside the cranium and the protective vertebral column. The 12 pairs of **cranial nerves** sit adjacent to the CNS but are technically considered peripheral. The two most important parts of the peripheral nervous system are the **somatic** (sensing and moving) and the **autonomic** system, which consists of two opposing forces: the **sympathetic** ("fight or flight") and the **parasympathetic** ("relax and rest") which balance and control nearly all our blood vessels and organ functions.

If you believe in evolution, then long ago, our ancestors weren't deep thinkers but little more than glorified feeding tubes. Before we had brains, we had **enteric** nervous systems or so-called "gut brains." In time, this older enteric system not only became connected to the more recently evolved autonomic nervous system but also to the immune and endocrine systems. The intestines are a site of massive production of neurotransmitters and are home to many kinds of bacteria.

If we are being honest, much of what we think we understand about cell biology is subject to the same biases as Ramón y Cajal. We take Polaroid snapshots and think we understand the music and the movements of the dance. The hidden language of persuasion is probably that many kinds of cells, under the right conditions, can magically repair or transform into something else.

DIVISIONS OF
THE NERVOUS SYSTEM

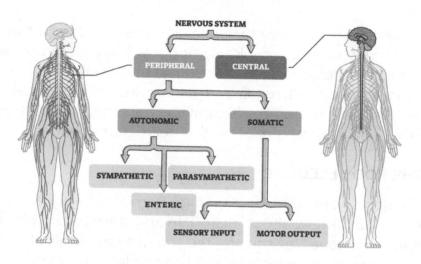

14.2: The Nervous Systems

NERVE REGENERATION AFTER STROKE OR NERVE DAMAGE

Remember those mice who were given strokes in Chapter 11? In 2012, an interesting study was published in which they gave mice strokes by surgically tying off one of their carotid arteries while under anesthesia. They found that MSC exosomes were released with miR-133b on the affected side. That particular microRNA is associated with the regrowth of **neurites** (dendrites and axons).[4]

Remember that Schwann cells maintain myelination on peripheral nerves? Scientists found that a crush injury to mice nerves caused the Schwann cells to change about four dozen micro RNAs. They found that the expression of two of the blocking micro RNAs dropped significantly. First, miR-34a, which is always expressed to block de-differentiation, drops significantly, allowing stem cells to become primitive (copying and directing repair like an embryonic cell). Secondly, after injury, they found a drop in miR-140, which blocks new myelin production.[5]

So what? So, we have brilliant scientists who found three notes in what is a complex symphony. It is a start, but we are kidding ourselves to believe the dogma that the nervous system can't repair or that we are on the verge of being able to reproduce natural mechanisms produced by MSCs and neural stem cells after nerve damage.

THE BODY ELECTRIC

We don't want to really disparage Ramón y Cajal because he couldn't know about microRNA and stem cell de-differentiation. Isaac Newton created the fundamentals of classical mechanics, which we still use to plan space voyages, but space-time and relativity had not yet been imagined/discovered. What the Spaniard did leave us was a model of electrical wiring forming relays; this still serves as a helpful model. He didn't know about neurotransmitters and microRNA because they hadn't been discovered yet.

Just as you wouldn't be surprised if a 70-yo told you they had wrinkles and hardened arteries, you wouldn't be surprised to hear that their mental flexibility and speed were not what they used to be. Thankfully, there is some ability to repair itself, but in general, the nerves are living cells that are OEM (original equipment manufacturer), and that means they can become genetically, metabolically, and physically damaged, causing them to become dysfunctional or non-functional. Since there is some redundancy, like the fiber bundles in the tendons or the cables of the Golden Gate Bridge, we can get away with some low-grade loss of function.

Why don't we just regrow or replace our nerves like a knee joint or a coronary artery? When they do open heart surgery, they can stop your heart and pump blood for you with a machine while they work. But we don't have the technology to stop your nervous system and replace sections of it because your nervous system is what is keeping you alive and conscious, and it was built to last a lifetime that currently, and thankfully, exceeds the OEM warranty. Just like with knee cartilage, your body does 100% of what it can to repair, using MSC exosomes and stem cell replication. However the repair results fall short of 100% original functioning. If you lose knee cartilage, you might reduce physical activity and not really notice. But if your brain cells or nerves are damaged, they might be causing missing, faulty, or unrelenting electrical signals that are harder to adjust to or ignore.

CHRONIC NEURALGIA (nerve pain)

My friend, Antonia, was a 61-year-old Brazilian shaman whom I met years earlier during an anti-aging conference where I was lecturing about telomerase. When I reunited with her in 2019, she told me that for the previous four years, she had suffered excruciating pain in the area of her lower left jaw (aka mandible). During a dental procedure, the dentist's hand and tool slipped, causing injury to the tongue and jaw. The pain was an eight out of ten, constant, and despite removing two healthy molar teeth, it never improved. In an attempt to remediate the problem, we injected a small amount of exosomes into the area around the inferior alveolar nerve, and within days, the pain was gone. It has remained gone for four years now.[6]

Another friend, 55-year-old Dr. GH, was a faculty member of the anti-aging conference whom I had also met years before. She contacted me earlier this year after her nurse had attended my exosome lecture because she hoped I could help with her trigeminal neuralgia. She had suffered the sudden onset of excruciating pain in the ophthalmic (upper face) branch of the trigeminal nerve. This resulted in excessive lacrimation, photophobia (light intolerance), and pain, requiring multiple medications to keep from being suicidal. Botox and migraine medications were tried and did not help. As luck would have it, I was meeting another patient with the same problem, so she was able to meet me by driving down to Miami from Orlando. We injected MSC exosomes nasally, and they must have diffused to the damaged areas of the fifth cranial nerve because her pain completely resolved shortly thereafter and has since been completely gone. Incidentally, the original patient with the trigeminal neuralgia, who had flown from the Bahamas to Miami, also received a nasal injection that improved his debilitating trigeminal neuralgia to nearly normal status.[7]

What could be accounting for the disappearance of nerve pain? If nerves are electrical wires and pain represents a "short circuit" of sorts, then processes triggered by MSC exosomes and their contents, like increased miR-133b (regrowth of neurites), decreased miR-34a (blocker of de-differentiation), and decrease of miR-140 (inhibitor of myelin production), may be acting like electrical tape on those live wires.

SENSORY ORGANS REPAIRED

RM was a 65-year-old man with 2.5 years of profound loss of light touch sensation in both feet immediately after a degreaser leaked into his work boots. He still had the perception of pain, temperature, and pressure, but he felt like his feet were wrapped in cellophane. Four weeks after the original insult, he developed a loss of touch sensation in the tips of his dominant hand after working with a high vibratory saw. My theory is that the degreaser, which is hydrophobic and can, therefore remain stored in fat for a long time, was still in his system to create a similar injury in his fingers. Light touch is sensed by a nerve ending coiled up inside pressure-sensing cells in tiny dermal structures called **Meissner's corpuscles**. The degreaser must have damaged those cells and/or removed the fatty myelin insulating sheaths of their nerves.

Using ultrasound, we were able to see the affected nerves. With a needle guided into the sheath of the nerves, MSC exosomes were injected with the hopes they would work their way down the nerves to the damaged Meissner's corpuscles. Within twelve hours, the patient was already improving. Within a month, the light touch sensation in the feet had returned to about a 7 of 10 and in the fingers to an 8 of 10. There has been some loss of sensation in the feet to 5 of 10 after three years, but he knows he can repeat as needed and is managing with intermittent fasting.[8]

BELL'S PALSY

Chances are you know someone with facial asymmetry. In general, if both the top and bottom are affected, it is a paralysis of the 7th cranial nerve, or Bell's palsy, which is believed to be caused by viral injury in many cases. Facial paralysis affecting only the lower face may be from a cerebral (brain) injury like a stroke because the upper face receives enervation (nerve signals) from both hemispheres of the brain. ES was a 69-year-old woman with a 12-year history of right-sided Bell's Palsy. We injected the area around the 7th cranial nerve with MSC exosomes, and the palsy resolved. I still use her before and after pictures in a booth display but since no one can believe it, they just give me dirty looks when they see it and walk on with disdain.

0Why would this improve? Just as with the live wires causing pain and the dead wires causing loss of light touch, nerves can be repaired if they receive the proper signals. Some of those signals may be present in MSC exosomes.[9]

Bell's Plasy (Cranial Nerve VII damage)

Before   10d after treatment

14.3: Bell's Palsy

FACE BLINDNESS

From the Greek words for face (prosopon) and not knowing (agnosia), we get **prosopagnosia**, or the inability to recognize faces. Specific damage to areas in the visual and associative parts of the brain can cause people to lose the ability to identify faces. An estimated 2.5% of people may have impaired or absent facial recognition abilities.

LG was a 48-yo woman who was selling me dry ice when she mentioned her condition. Since her first pregnancy 14 years prior, she had struggled to recognize the people she saw all the time, like parents of her children's friends. After a treatment with nasal and intravenous exosomes, she recovered much of her facial recognition ability and is now more comfortably navigating social situations.[10]

TINNITUS

Perceiving noises that aren't there, like ringing or whooshing, is known as **tinnitus** (TIN-ni-tus) if they are not hallucinatory in nature. Damage can occur in the sensing organ of the **cochlea** (snail-shaped organ of hearing), the 8th cranial (aka **vestibulocochlear**) nerves, or the brain cortex itself. In the case of 79-year-old KH, she had suffered 22 years of 8 out of 10 hissing from both ears that was unrelenting. It started after a period of tremendous life stress. Within two weeks of nasal and intravenous injections, her tinnitus disappeared entirely on one side and nearly 80% on the other.[11]

Sometimes, there is an associated condition of noise sensitivity called **hyperacusis** (hai-pur-uh-KYOO-suhs). When there is damage to cranial nerves 5 and 7, the control of two specific muscles in the middle ear can become impaired. Normally, the transmission of loud noises is reflexively dampened by both the:

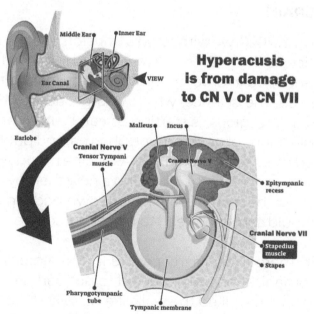

14.4: Sound Sensitivity (Hyperacusis)

1. the **tensor tympani** muscle attached to the first inner ear bone of the **malleus** (attached to the tympanic membrane) and controlled by the 5th cranial nerve

2. the **stapedius** muscle, controlled by the 7th cranial nerve, which tightens the third **stapes** bone (attached to the snail or cochlea via the oval window)

A couple of times a month, I have new patients contact me about tinnitus with or without hyperacusis. Although the science is far from settled, some patients seem to have difficulty with the Covid spike protein expressed by the virus and in the mRNA vaccinations.[12] There may be damage to small vessels which feed nerves that is causing small fiber neuropathy. To be honest, treatments using both trans-tympanic and nasal techniques with MSC exosomes are usually NOT successful for tinnitus and hyperacusis. That said, there are cases where stem cells or exosomes have improved what is essentially an incurable condition.

COVID BRAIN

Beginning in 2020, we witnessed a transformation in the way we practice as doctors. Conservatism and informed consent were abandoned in order to try to mitigate fear. As the years have passed, the science, which was political to the point of becoming religious, is starting to catch up. Whereas the major institutions of government, pharma, and public health exempted themselves from mRNA vaccine mandates, many found themselves faced with taking a new therapy based on an unproven theory that having your own body make spike protein would somehow lead to better outcomes.

Although there likely many people in the aforementioned exempt organizations who elected to not partake, JD was a 60-yo man who walked the walk like he talked the talk. As a pharmaceutical executive, he took two Pfizer mRNA shots, contracted the Delta variant in July of 2021, and as a result, lost his sense of smell. Then, in the fall of 2021, he got a multivalent booster mRNA shot. In 2022, he took two Moderna mRNA shots and then contracted Covid again in March 2023.

Beginning in December 2021, he began suffering memory loss, brain fog, and problems with communication (aphasia). When he went to the Mayo Clinic's "Long Covid" program, they confirmed his brain was affected with small vessel **ischemia** (ee-SKEE-mee-uh) or cell death. There was one small dead area and a generalized loss of cortex volume. The Mayo Clinic recommended nutraceuticals but warned against trying MSC exosomes.

After an extensive review of his records and a lengthy and complex informed consent, JD decided to try the MSC exosomes in a combination of intravenous, nasal, and intraspinal injections. At about six weeks, he felt like a cloud was lifting in his cognition, and his energy level was improved.

In contrast to the Mayo Clinic, there is a Dr. Askenazy at Yale University, who has been treating long Covid brain with MSC exosomes and has published his findings.[13] Interestingly, this academic, myself, and many colleagues have been having good results in treating post Covid syndromes, which appear to be from a neuro-immunological process that is capable of causing brain damage.

OF MICE AND MEN

If you recall Chapter 11, the benefits of treating acute stroke with MSC exosomes in mice were clear. But what happens when you treat people with longstanding CNS deficits from older injuries? The first patient I treated had been a victim of spinal cord paralysis from a motorcycle accident four years prior. JP was a 45-year-old man with no movement or sensation below the nipples (spinal thoracic level T4). We performed an intraspinal injection of MSC exosomes, and within weeks, he was starting to feel slightly painful sensations in his abdomen, and there were some involuntary movements in the legs in response to painful stimuli. The patient declined to repeat injections, and we don't really know what the best outcome might have been with unlimited resources because of the severe nature of spinal cord injury.

DK was a 59-year-old man who suffered a stroke five years prior that put him into a three-month coma and a lengthy rehab. He was left with weakness in his left face and body, complex regional pain syndrome, and right-sided blindness. After a nasal injection, he recovered the ability to see movement but still could not clearly make out shapes. His blood pressure and constipation also improved.

DK referred a friend's wife, LI, a 50-yo who had a massive stroke a year earlier. She was unable to move or feel on the left side. An autologous stem cell treatment in Japan had done little to improve her. The first treatment with intravenous and nasal MSC exosomes resulted in an overnight recovery of the ability to move her left shoulder and bear some weight on the left hip. I will never forget it. Over the course of the next two days, she recovered some ability to dorsiflex her left foot. A second shot improved her lower arm rotation. A third shot was given, and her proprioception and spasticity improved. At some point, she felt the progress didn't justify the expense, so again, we will never know how far she could have recovered if she had continued therapy.

Similar to the immune derangement covered in the next chapter, I am guarded in my prognosis for spinal cord injury and stroke. Trying to repair complex damaged systems, unlike isolated nerves, has a poor prognosis unless they are given early, as in the mice experiments, when the inflammation is high and the damage is new. If you are only going to recover 20% of function, no matter what you do, is it worth it? Perhaps someday, specific neural stem cell-derived exosomes will be more helpful.

A SMILING BABY

I just received my first message after three months of not hearing from a dad who had contacted me five months prior. His now 8-month-old son was smiling! He texted me: "Exosomes have helped tremendously to improve his mood and cognition. He is a very happy baby and smiles so much now. [His auditory nerves] are functioning totally normally after failing in both ears a few months ago."

When this dad contacted me at 3 months of age, he was distraught. His son was irritable, spastic, and deaf. The tests showed severe brain damage and a 90% chance of developing cerebral palsy. The child had low oxygen from a home breech delivery, and it took 45 minutes to reach the hospital. Doctors induced a hypothermic coma, but the neurological damage was severe. Because they lived outside my practice jurisdictions and because I couldn't find a doctor nearby to help, I recommended he obtain frozen exosomes and administer them as a weekly nasal inhalation, which he has done from 5 to 8 months of age.

The colicky nature and lack of social interaction have improved. He smiles, and his deafness has resolved. Is it likely that he will have cerebral palsy? Yes. But with the neuroplasticity of an infant using the healing advantage of MSC exosomes from a newborn source, perhaps his future will be quite different than the experts would have imagined.

Is the inhalation of nasal exosomes approved by the FDA for anoxic birth injury? No. Is it being tested? No. Is there evidence from animal studies that it would help? Yes. If it were your son, what would you do with such a dismal prognosis yet clear improvements after trying the MSC exosomes?

Chapter 15

ANECDOTES IN IMMUNE DYSFUNCTION

[Instead] of inquiring why the Roman empire
was destroyed,
we should rather be surprised that it had
subsisted so long.

—Edward Gibbon,
author of *The History of the Decline and
Fall of the Roman Empire*

Think of your immune system as the Roman Empire; casual historians might believe that it fell victim to Goth invaders, but in fact, the Goth generals became the mercenary army and helped to destroy the empire from within. When we are no longer able to discern friend from foe and suppress invaders, problems arise.

If you were confused by Chapter 9 on the immune system, join the club. The immune system is capable of upregulating in many different ways to respond to totally different kinds of threats, but it also has to actively downregulate those pathways so it doesn't become unbalanced or create collateral damage.

The practice of medicine is not easy. There is a lot to memorize, a lot to understand, and then there is the risk. By listening to and examining the patients, most conditions can be reliably diagnosed, and the physical examination will be used to confirm the working theories of what is causing your problems. The use of lab tests and imaging with things like ultrasound, X-rays, and MRIs can be helpful, but a good clinician can usually determine what is wrong with you just by listening and doing a simple physical exam.

Although we would like to think that there is very little error, the truth is that it is often a matter of using observation, intuition, probability, and even empirical treatments to practice medicine. Luckily, many conditions, if not made worse by our interventions, will become better with the body's own processes, although as we noted with tendinosis and arthrosis, the body may not be repairing all the way back to 100% but rather accumulating damage as we get older and get repeatedly injured.

When it comes to problems affecting the immune system, the first two paragraphs above no longer apply. If the immune system is chronically infected, challenged, depleted, suppressed, or distracted, the reasons for disease can be too complex to understand with a single explanation. What works one time might cause a severe reaction the next time it is tried. Although a sprained ankle ligament might recover to the point of being ignored, an immune system that is deranged is something that will not be ignored. While I would have no hesitation in giving exosomes for a simple autoimmune disease, some patients have too many things going on to expect a striking improvement with only MSC exosomes.

WATERLOO

Napoleon was a brilliant general, yet when faced with a superior coalition of enemies, he was defeated at the Battle of Waterloo. Whereas the arthritic knee, the tennis elbow, the cold feet, and the isolated nerves have often been vanquished by MSC exosomes in my experience of over 1800 injections, there are some instances in which we have been rebuffed. Although you will hear some patients and doctors declare victory against enemies like Lyme (*Borellia*), *Bartonella*, fungi and molds, and human herpesviruses, I would advise caution based on my own limited experience using MSC exosomes in complex, immune-deranged patients.

An emerging reality in today's toxic world is that many of us have problems that are complex, multifactorial, and not easily understood in a single reductionist fashion. Despite having a master's in public health, I am mostly agnostic when it comes to beliefs about things like vaccine injury, 5G electromagnetic waves, GMO foods, glyphosate, and gain-of-function research to increase the virulence of pathogens. Because many doctors lack the knowledge, specialized testing, patience, or humility to manage complex cases, patients often look to online support groups of varying qualities and to alternative practitioners of varying skills.

A typical "Waterloo" patient might present like this: middle-aged, low energy, intestinal problems, diagnosed with fungal toxins and possible *Borellia*, non-specific mood and cognitive problems, and possibly pain in joints. They feel better if they eliminate things like dairy and gluten and eat only red meat. And, they have spent many hours on the internet because the medical establishment cannot juggle multiple problems without one clear causation that is resulting in their immune dysfunction.

It is hard to determine in most cases whether these opportunistic problems are the cause or the result of immune dysfunction. The majority of people who get bitten by a Lyme-infested tick do NOT develop chronic Lyme disease. Despite having herpesviruses in our bodies and being exposed to fungi everywhere, healthy people don't get shingles or have detectable levels of fungal toxins. Yet the distraction, exhaustion, and often the actual organisms can infect and affect lymphocyte function, so these opportunistic infections are **both the cause and the result of immune dysregulation.**

If the insult to the patient's nervous system was in the remote past, let's say a black mold in your drywall years ago that was removed, followed by negative blood tests after taking antifungal medicines, then I would be comfortable treating them with immune modulatory (read suppressive) MSC exosomes.

On the other hand, I often turn away patients who haven't even tried the mainstream medical treatments for something like active chronic Lyme, because I don't want to make matters worse.

PULMONARY FIBROSIS

Up until this point in the book, we have shared promising animal studies and human anecdotes. Now is the time to explain why complex, immune-deranged patients are not easily helped with MSC exosomes. SH was a 74-year-old man diagnosed with idiopathic pulmonary fibrosis of at least six years duration. The most notable finding on his exam, other than the persistent cough and low oxygenation, was the nail fungus that had infested his toenails for twenty years. We treated him with intravenous and inhaled nebulized exosomes (after bronchodilation). Unfortunately, the lungs did not improve. Areas such as the low back and cold feet did respond to local MSC exosome injections, but the root problems of nail fungus and lung disease were not improved.

Ironically, the lung specialist recommended a medication based on a mold toxin, to suppress his immune system, despite it not being clear that an autoimmune problem was at the heart of his lung disease. In my mind, he already had ample immune suppression from the existing fungal infection. In fact, those toxins may have caused his lung disease. Battling that fungus for over twenty years may have depleted and deranged his immune system too much, and the ongoing damage may have depleted the reserves of lung stem cells needed to potentially regenerate.

CHRONIC LYME

KR was a 58-year-old woman diagnosed with Lyme disease 12 years prior with severe neurological problems which were misattributed to multiple sclerosis. The Lyme had caused sleep problems, progressive autonomic dysfunction, spasticity on the left, decreased core strength, and general loss of muscle tone and hand dexterity. When I met her, she was being treated for mold, Lyme (*Borrelia*), *Bartonella,* and *Babesia* (a protozoan infection of red blood cells) by an alternative health clinic using glutathione, alpha lipoic acid, and phosphatidylcholine. These are not FDA-approved, but some practitioners feel they can be helpful. I am sad to report that my administration of intravenous MSC exosomes appeared to do nothing to improve her symptoms.

THE ROAD TO HANA

JK was a 39-year-old mother, civil rights attorney, and yoga instructor who contacted me to try MSC exosomes.

She developed a fungal breast infection one month prior to a Moderna mRNA injection in July of 2021. Within a few weeks, she was having muscle fasciculations and esophageal spasms, leading to vomiting. Brain fog and depressed mood led her to a meat diet, which initially improved her condition, but then, she had a sudden worsening from a possible **Herxheimer** reaction (toxic inflammation from dying of pathogens). This was experienced as worsening skin crawling (**paresthesia**), diffuse muscle spasms, and even sexual excitation after eating. Despite being given the mRNA shot, she also contracted COVID-19 (Omicron variant) six months later.

Her workup discovered *Toxoplasmosis, Rickettsia*, Lyme (*Borrelia), Bartonella,* and *Babesia*. She also was strongly positive for anti-spike antibodies (COVID-19 capsule protein) and antibodies for TS/HDS (trisulfated heparin disaccharide), which have been associated with small fiber neuropathy.[1]

Armed with a freezer filled with MSC exosomes and good intentions, I flew to Maui and drove the 3-hour trip to Hana. Despite nasal, intravenous, and intrathecal exosomes, her condition did not improve.

CLUES FROM FAILURE

I started this chapter by stating that the practice of medicine is difficult, but hopefully, these three cases illustrate how, in the case of immune derangement, the practice is made even more challenging. What can we say about these three "Waterloo" patients?

Firstly, the existence of the opportunistic infections named above is not easily diagnosed, given the myriad of different testing regimens with controversial predictive values. Secondly, having those conditions negatively impacts the host's immune system, engendering more opportunistic infections. Thirdly, chronic immune suppression might hinder favorable immune responses that typically might be triggered by MSC exosomes. Fourth, the inflammatory response to any infection, but especially COVID-19 infection and its spike protein, can cause an opening of the blood-brain barrier, leading to neuroinflammation.[2] Lastly, these patients are often faced with extreme difficulty finding help since their problems tend to be complex, hard to definitively diagnose and treat, and have guarded prognoses when it comes to complete remission.

Even my patient, who is a drug company CEO, received only shoulder shrugs and nutritional supplements when diagnosed with "Long Covid" and severe cognitive damage, which likely resulted from five mRNA shots and two bouts with Covid. That is nothing compared to a patient who called me about her 14-year-old's sudden inability to walk, which was deemed to be psychosomatic by a board-certified neurologist without doing any blood tests, spinal tap, or imaging. If she had only lied and said her daughter's problems began after a tick bite rather than an mRNA shot, she might have received a totally different workup. Doctors are not immune from cognitive dissonance, especially if they are seeing a lot of patients claiming neurological injury from Covid or its vaccination.

What can we do to help these patients? Unfortunately, the best thing we can do is to empower them. Since no one is going to care as much as their friends and family, they need to become "Dr. Google" as much as we professionals might use that term with skepticism.

Something that helps to detoxify might trigger that aforementioned Herxheimer reaction because infected cells burst open like toxic piñatas. That could include antibiotics,

Ozone or hyperbaric oxygen, and light therapies. It is worth considering pretreatment with so-called binders like charcoal, chlorella blue-green algae, zeolites, and bentonite clays if you are anticipating a Herxheimer reaction. Also, having an appropriate antibiotic on board at the time of therapy might prevent reseeding if those piñatas burst.

If they haven't been tested for **MTHFR (methylenetetrahydrofolate reductase)** gene defects, they should make sure they have two normal gene copies as I am finding immune derangement to be associated with this mutation. Glutathione can help remediate this and is topically available from my website.

They need to "trust but verify" and be skeptical of providers who quote very high success rates without wanting to discuss failures. I would never say that any case is hopeless, but to prevail, the patient and caregivers need to be honest, creative, resilient, and tenacious.

THE EXCEPTION THAT PROVES THE RULE

Before we close this gloomy chapter, I will leave you with a happier case of the exception that proves the rule about failure in complex cases. RS was a 48-year-old man who came with friends to try intravenous exosome therapy. He really had no expectations that it would help, but he was suffering from multiple food intolerances for four years. After eating anything, he would have yellowish diarrhea and cramps, followed by itching. As a result of what was called MCAS (mast cell activation syndrome), he had eczema on his hands.

What was not expected was that in the weeks after taking intravenous MSC exosomes, not only did his food intolerance disappear, but his eczema, spider veins, and facial bloating resolved, making him look twenty years younger. When I show his face on my conference pop-up banner, people get mad at me. I didn't ask him to photo document his changes, but he did so anyway. Three years later, he still tells us that his appearance is normal and that his spider veins, eczema, and food intolerance are gone.[3]

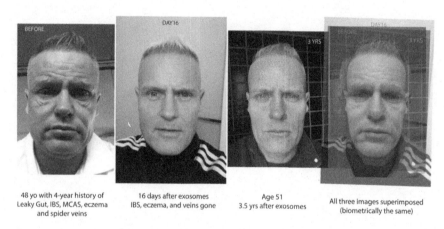

| 48 yo with 4-year history of Leaky Gut, IBS, MCAS, eczema and spider veins | 16 days after exosomes IBS, eczema, and veins gone | Age 51 3.5 yrs after exosomes | All three images superimposed (biometrically the same) |

15.1: Leaky Gut caused mast cell activation syndrome (MCAS)

Why did he improve? Most likely, the tight junctions in his intestines were not tight enough to prevent digested food particles from entering his bloodstream. Those particles triggered mast cell activation, which led to his dermatitis. The spider vein resolution was probably just from endothelial repair described in Chapter 13. Finally, the lack of facial swelling from histamines accounts for the restoration of his preferred, youthful appearance.

Speaking of youthful appearances, the following chapter will cover some of the aspects of what many would consider vanity over health, but as Billy Crystal's Saturday Night Live character used to say, "It's better to look good than to feel good. You know who you are."

Chapter 16

OTHER TREATMENT ANECDOTES

We must always change, renew, rejuvenate
ourselves;
otherwise, we harden.

—Goethe (poet, playwright, and scientist)

If you have understood the book thus far, you will understand that MSC exosomes are the body's main mechanism of repair, but we never quite get back to 100% of where
we used to be. The privilege of getting older is associated
with acquiring cell aging and dysfunction. If your insides
are young and beautiful, your outsides probably are as well.
There is no great skill to look young when you are a teenager, but to look young when you are old? Well, that is the
stuff that business empires are made of.

Before we talk about cosmetics, let's review some of the
ways in which we can use exosomes. To date, I have treated
nearly 400 patients in over 700 different encounters, utiliz-
ing a total of 1800 different procedures. Although my record
keeping has some faults, like counting an ankle injection
as a ligament and forgetting to record it as an ankle, I keep
a running tally of everything as well as a spreadsheet with
names, dates of birth, procedures, lot numbers, and reactions reported.

What I will convey is that with the single brand that I've used, there have been no adverse reactions of an allergic nature. That is probably because they have no additives, no endotoxin, no MHC antigens to trigger an immune response, and they are anti-inflammatory by nature. Nevertheless, I always see patients armed with epinephrine, Benadryl, smelling salts, a pulse oximeter, and other first-aid precautions.

I did have one patient develop a knee infection that could have occurred with a joint injection of anything, such as steroids or hyaluronic acid. The most common adverse reaction would be cold sore (HSV-1) reactivation, which might occur somewhere around one in fifteen patients. For that reason, I will often give 1 gram of valacyclovir at the time of treatment, and I always stress that patients call me immediately for numbness or tingling in previous areas of cold sores.

The most common procedures in descending order are nasal (355), intravenous (344), fingers/toes (223), knees (189), shoulder (99), nerves (73), arterial (61), facial (61), lumbar epidural (61), muscles/tendons/ligaments (47), wrists (32), penis (23), and intraspinal (29). That said, we have also done procedures ranging from topical ophthalmic, inhaled nebulized, intraperitoneal, trans-tympanic, dental, and vaginal.

The word panacea, carries a negative connotation because the assumption is that there is nothing that can cure everything, right? Well, with the exception of complex immune derangement cases, I have found that MSC exosomes start to approach something similar to a true panacea. If Mother Nature intended stem cells to be able to heal all cell types with downregulation of inflammation, increased vascularity, and local stem cell proliferation, then using what she made in the same fashion but higher doses, seems to make sense for many conditions.

FACIAL REJUVENATION

I just got off the phone with a physician friend of mine who was telling me that a PRP "vampire" facial didn't seem to do anything for her. I don't do PRP facials, but when I listen to those that do, they generally state that PRP from older blood tends to be less effective for all uses. Since she is on immunosuppressives for Crohn's disease, it is also possible that her normal response to the inflammation that PRP is supposed to create was blunted. Recall that the reason microneedling with PRP works is because of inflammation, which begets stem cells, which excrete exosomes. If the inflammation is blunted and the PRP is from a weak source, then you get less of your own MSCs, with their older exosomes, to the skin where you want to stimulate regrowth. If they warn you, "Don't take even Tylenol, ibuprofen, or aspirin after PRP because we want inflammation," what do you think immunosuppressive therapy would do?

When we do microneedling, we will naturally trigger inflammation, which draws in stem cells to quiet and control the inflammation. Then, those stem cells will secrete your exosomes to stop inflammation and heal the area. However many providers and patients are finding that if they introduce extra exosomes at the time of the procedures, you get better results than from just your 100% capacity of exosome secretion. That makes sense because you are giving orders of magnitude more of the homologous signaling that would typically be made.

In case you are interested, the FDA has approved microneedling for cosmetic purposes and states it is proven to help with scars and wrinkles for persons over the age of 22. The addition of more of exosomes than your body will make to heal is admittedly NOT FDA approved, yet it makes sense that more is more if we want a stronger response and a younger appearance.

In the practice of cosmetic dermatology, there are many of you who are already well-initiated. That is because people generally do see positive results. Gone are the days of deep CO_2 laser or chemical peels with their very long recovery times. The trend currently is for multiple, commoditized treatments by a technician with lasers or microneedling (with or without radiofrequency). The common denominator is that when damaged, the skin can heal with newer collagens and result in a younger appearance via thickening of the dermis from new collagen and extracellular matrix deposition and also the destruction of pigmented lesions.

Everyone who spends tens of thousands of dollars buying the latest in technology will advocate specific procedures to recoup their costs. But what we need to understand is that the addition of naturally occurring but more potent MSC exosomes would likely improve all outcomes, regardless of the energetic, ablative, or penetrative "damage" method that is used.

Typically, a person will have 20-30 minutes of anesthesia cream applied to their face before washing it off. That will numb the face enough to tolerate most procedures, but if there is deeper penetration required or the pain tolerance is low, then nitrous oxide (laughing gas) is sometimes added. What is interesting is that instead of the seven or more days of redness, peeling, and even weeping skin from older chemical peels and CO_2 laser resurfacing, the addition of true MSC exosomes is so anti-inflammatory that they can be considered "zero downtime" procedures. For most, they can go out with light makeup the next day, and they might look like they had only a mild sunburn. People with darker complexions have traditionally risked post-inflammatory hyperpigmentation, but since MSC exosomes are so anti-inflammatory, they might render many of the ablative lasers safer for those folks.

Buyer beware! Because of material costs, most cosmetic practices currently use freeze-dried exosome products, which have much less viability and efficacy. They probably do contain remnants of protein and mRNA that are somewhat beneficial as an adjunct to all facial rejuvenation procedures. The cost of microneedling is usually the least, and it is largely painless, with little downtime, especially if used with cryopreserved, not freeze-dried, MSC exosomes. The actual charge to you will depend on the practice's costs and its business model/ethics. To learn more about facial rejuvenation, see this blog.[1]

HAIR RESTORATION

I won't belabor the point, so to answer your question, "Does this really work?" the answer is a resounding "sometimes!" There are many providers who are claiming good responses. I don't do the procedure much in my practice, but that is likely because I don't know how to package and sell it.

Of my 15 or so attempts to remediate alopecia, I would say there was no significant improvement in 10 of them, partial improvement in 4, and nearly complete resolution in one. The fault is largely my own. There are no professionals doing single treatments for alopecia since the nature of hair growth is that the hairs are in different phases. I should have arranged for packages of multiple sessions.

Because loss of hair is multifactorial, we can say that certain types are more easily remediated than others. If there is terminal differentiation of hair stem cells and scarring of the connective tissues, the hope is less. In contrast, acute hair loss after a bout with Covid or an autoimmune flare could respond better because the root cause (pun intended) is inflammatory and perhaps a loss of small vessel circulation.

MSC exosomes can stimulate stem cells in hair follicles.[2] Interestingly, a fairly common reaction to intravenous exosomes can also be repigmentation of hair, which I also have seen with telomerase activation even in a 114-yo.[3]

The subject of hair growth and loss is too complicated to cover here, but I will leave you with the third of my before/after pictures which earn me thousands of dirty looks at professional conferences. Please forgive the lower-quality image, as it is a screenshot from a lost PowerPoint. Also, I decided to replace the before picture, which was with wet hair, so it looked more sparse. The irony is that this particular patient attributes his regrowth to Minoxidil. When I asked my hair restoration colleagues about that explanation, they were skeptical. To learn more about hair loss and exosomes, watch this webinar.[4]

KW, 62 with MSK problems and MPB
Exosomes are NOT FDA-approved to treat hair loss

- 5/20 Initial "overhaul"
2.5 B each subacromial bursa with 1.5cc Euflexxa
5B epidural at L4 (pt placed Tberg for 10 minutes)
2.5B each nasal inf turbinate after topical viscous lido and iodine prep.
2.5B IV
2.5B each knee with 1.5cc Durolane HA
0.3B left ankle
4.7B divided into each plantar fascia 2cm distal to calcaneus in three sites at approx 5-8mm depth

- 7/20 2BMSC +2B AF microneedled
- 12/20 minoxidil
- Previous minoxidil success 20 ya
- Now hair improved

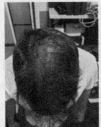

16.1: Hair restoration in a patient treated with exosomes

SEXUAL DYSFUNCTION – VENUS AND MARS

Let's say that you've gotten your face looking younger, and your silky locks have grown back. Now, the younger partners seem interested, but you aren't sure if you can perform! Thankfully, the exosome "Genie" has more than two wishes for you.

As a trained Gynecologist, I'll take on female sexual dysfunction first. Sexual desire in women, as with men, seems to be related not only to androgens (male sex hormones) but to general health, self-perception, and complex psycho/social/spiritual factors. That said, sexual function experts tell us that 10% of women have NEVER had an orgasm and that less than 20% of women have orgasms from vaginal penetrative sex if they don't also have clitoral stimulation. What seems most correlated with the ability to climax is the number of times the couple has partnered, arguing for the beneficial effects of feeling relaxed for most women. Only 11% of women had orgasms the first time with a partner, whereas 67% did when the relationship was longer than six months.[5]

Dyspareunia (painful sex) and vulvodynia (vulvar pain) are notable problems for many women, although in the absence of physical pathology or a history of abuse, they are often episodic. Common causes would be infections or lack of sexual excitation and its concomitant lubrication and increased blood flow. Unfortunately, for women of advanced age who have been long deprived of estrogen, the loss of circulation and thinning of the vulvovaginal structures can make dyspareunia a simple fact of aging. Even for the woman who has a concern over taking systemic estrogens, the use of a topical estrogen cream can be transformative for genitourinary health and function.

Some practices inject exosomes into areas such as the vulva, the clitoris, and even the "G-spot" on the anterior vaginal wall. Especially in the case of atrophy and pain, there is little reason to believe that improved circulation and regeneration of local stem cells wouldn't occur. The procedure was typically done using PRP, but as with other PRP treatments into the face or MSK uses, we no longer require the inflammation of PRP to bring MSCs to secrete their exosomes; we just add exosomes from the start.

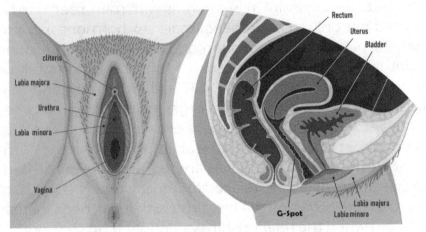

Vaginal rejuvenation: Clitoris, G-Spot, around urethra, vulva

16.2: Female Genital Injection Sites

If you are otherwise doing great in your sexual communication and genital health, then injections with MSC exosomes would probably help since most tissues seem to be rejuvenated. Improved circulation and enervation will be more effective if the tissues are not already atrophic from prolonged lack of estrogen. Notably, stress urinary incontinence is a frequent problem in older women that can also be addressed with exosome rejuvenation.

That said, if you and your partner don't cooperate well inside the bedroom, then injections to improve the physical function probably wouldn't make the biggest difference. I would use topical vaginal estrogen cream to keep the tissues healthy and perhaps attend a few sessions of sex therapy to openly discuss ways that relations could be improved.

NOW, FOR THE MEN

Speaking of Mars, you may not have realized that Mars' pointy symbol from Roman astrology is a literal phallic symbol. It is estimated that 95% of men are able to reach orgasm, but if the erection is not sufficiently hard or long-lasting, problems can occur. As with the post-menopausal vagina, the knee cartilage, the arteries, the nervous system, and our immune armies, the penis gets old too.

The primary issue with erectile function is damage to small vessels, although nerve damage, as in the case of prostate surgery or trauma from bicycle seats, can also play significant roles. As comedian Larry David's character from *Curb Your Enthusiasm* joked when asked if he believed in miracles, "I feel like every erection is a miracle."

As men age, the ability to maintain an erection until orgasm declines because of accumulated damage to nerves and vessels. Sexual function is under the general influence of androgens, which contribute to libido. The specific nerve pathway to maintain an erection is controlled by the parasympathetic ("rest and relax") nervous system, although the orgasm is directed by its opposite, the sympathetic ("fight or flight") system. The mnemonic is therefore "point (P) and shoot (S)" for those two systems. Damage to the spinal cord can cause problems with erectile function as well.

Every erection is basically a **compartment syndrome** of the penis. Rarely, when a thigh is traumatized, and an artery is torn open, high-pressure arterial bleeding into the muscle causes the leg to expand but the fascia can't expand with the increased pressure. This causes the softer veins to close and the pressure must be released by cutting the fascia, which is like a sausage casing.

The sexual imagination, or perhaps just feedback from a full bladder at night, causes a signal to be sent via the parasympathetic nerve to cause increased blood flow by vasodilation. It accomplishes this by muscle relaxation in the penile artery walls, which creates an increased pressure in the two large chambers that hold blood called the corpora cavernosa. Just as in a leg compartment syndrome, the increased pressure of blood closes off the softer veins, allowing for the buildup of pressure. Unlike a leg compartment syndrome from trauma, you don't want or need someone to cut the fascia to release the pressure.

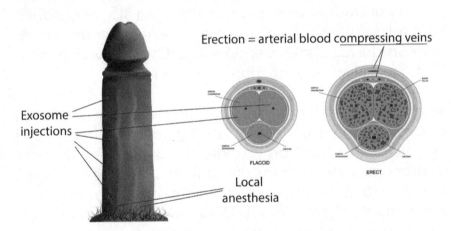

16.3: Erectile dysfunction and treatment sites

So, age-related vascular decline causes the hardening of the arteries and the loss of ability to relax enough to allow increased flow. Loss of nerve function is also a problem.

Is there any evidence, other than the patients whom we have treated, to suggest exosomes would help? Researchers created a rat model of erectile dysfunction using surgical nerve damage and measuring stimulated penile pressure four weeks after surgery. The rats treated with rat MSC exosomes or MSCs themselves recovered erectile function almost to the level of the sham (never performed) surgery and much more than the saline, placebo group.[6]

The penile injection procedures for ED had previously been performed using inflammation from PRP, as with the female shot, joints and tendons, and facial aesthetic treatments. The rat study above showed almost equal outcomes whether you had MSCs or just the MSC exosomes. So, instead of harvesting stem cells or needing blood, centrifugation, and "old platelets," we can just cut to the chase and use MSC exosomes from a newborn placental source.

The procedure tends to be a little painful because it is difficult to numb the penis completely by injecting around the penile nerves alone. It is also important to never use epinephrine to prevent ischemia (death by loss of blood flow). The mnemonic for never using epinephrine-containing local anesthesia is "fingers, nose, penis, toes" and if you are receiving any treatment in those areas, even as a patient, you should make sure providers never use local anesthesia from red bottles, which have vasoconstricting epinephrine inside. Nevertheless, if we use a short-acting local anesthetic, we can usually get the pain level down to about a 3 out of 10.

MISCELLANEOUS OTHER TREATMENTS

There are many other conditions that could benefit from decreased inflammation, increased vasculature, and local stem cell proliferation. In previous chapters, we discussed circulatory, MSK, neurological, and now aesthetic and sexual treatments.

Other treatments have included ophthalmic drops for uveitis and possible help with eye health, wrist injections for arthritis and carpal tunnel, tendon nodules for trigger fingers, plantar fasciitis, lumbar epidural for low back pain, for gout flares, and even ingested for a gastric ulcer. Was everyone helped? No. But I would estimate that at least 70% experienced some improvements.

Although not FDA-approved to treat aesthetic and sexual health, the marketplace has already adopted PRP treatments. If it weren't for the costs of purchasing exosomes, practitioners would likely prefer the use of MSC exosomes for these indications because of the lack of elicited pain and inflammation as well as the predictable results.

Chapter 17

ADVICE TO PATIENTS

Diligence is the mother of good luck.

—Benjamin Franklin

As we finish up the book, I want to summarize what we've learned and point you in the right direction regarding learning more and how to think about seeking your own treatments with MSC exosomes.

In the first chapter, we learned that exosomes are a new paradigm for understanding cell communication. In the subsequent chapters, we acquired the basic information to understand the fundamentals of cell biology with a specific interest in the role of stem cells generally and the MSC stem cell, in particular. We then discussed the history of regenerative medicine, from prolotherapy, PRP, stem cells, and now their final common pathway, exosomes. We learned about how exosomes are extracted and that there is no such thing as good or bad exosomes; they merely reflect the cellular ecology that is occurring.

In Chapter 7, we took a deeper dive into theories of aging and, in doing so, learned that the same principles of telomere attrition, epigenetic silencing, and stem cell dysfunction and depletion are at the root cause of all the manifestations of aging. Chapter 8 explained that "osis" is merely the accumulation of exhausted local stem cells in tissues like joint cartilage, tendons, and bones.

Chapter 9 was an introduction to the complexities of our immune systems. Chapter 10 discussed the FDA and whether exosomes can ever become a commercially available therapy given the financial and intellectual property constraints that exist.

Chapter 11 explored just a few of the thousands of scientific articles validating the benefits of MSC exosomes in animal models of disease. The following three chapters explored some promising anecdotes in treatment of actual patients, whereas the fourth chapter in this sequence described the types of difficult patients who present with immune derangement and are more resistant to the positive effects of exosome use. The preceding chapter explored cosmetic, sexual, and miscellaneous problems that might be helped by MSC exosome use.

If you've made it this far, I hope we can agree on a few things. Firstly, you have a better understanding of how biology works and why we accumulate dysfunctions as we age. Secondly, if animal studies and anecdotes can be believed, then conditions for which medicine currently has no treatments could potentially be helped by implementing MSC exosomes. Finally, there is a lot that you still don't understand. Before you pick up the phone to book an exosome treatment, let's discuss some important considerations.

CAVEAT EMPTOR

The Latin expression above translates into "let the buyer beware." Since healthcare payers rarely, if ever, compensate for non-FDA-approved treatments like MSC exosomes, you are facing significant out-of-pocket expenses. As with any decision, there is some due diligence required. Firstly, it wouldn't hurt to do a web search on PubMed to see what research exists on MSC exosomes and your particular condition. You may be surprised to know there are dozens of articles that you can understand, at least in the major points of the abstract (the summary of the article).

Secondly, you should look for online reviews of providers, search the National Provider Data Bank, and the state medical board website for adverse reporting. A personal referral from someone who has been to the practice you find can also be helpful.

Although practices may vary with regard to accessing the provider, I find it most helpful to speak with a potential patient, and I would hope the provider will also spare some time to understand your case. Avoid a treatment "mill" where you are shuffled through the system before you actually interact with the person who needs to understand your condition and work collaboratively with you. It might not be a good fit, and if someone doesn't have time to speak with you before, what do you think the follow-up will be like?

All doctors, including myself, are never equally comfortable doing all types of procedures. A competent grade school substitute teacher may be able to fill in for most classes. Still, when it comes to things like intraperitoneal or trans-tympanic injections, comfort level is a delicate balance between experience, skill, and risk management. Although it can be slightly off-putting, there are polite ways to assess this. Rather than ask, "How many of these have you done?" you could ask, "How comfortable are you with treating my condition?" We used to say in residency, "It's not how many you've done that matters; it's how many you

NEED to have done to feel comfortable and that remains true.

Here are some general "red flags" when it comes to dealing with providers.

- You can never get them on the phone.
- They don't actively listen but instead seem to incorrectly finish your sentences.
- They refuse to estimate your chances of getting better and instead imply that everyone is completely satisfied after treatments.
- They don't want to discuss various treatment options or different dosing and brands. If they are stuck with one brand, one dose, and don't consider the allopathic options, they may be overly rigid.

LOCATION, LOCATION, LOCATION

In cases of acute injury (trauma, surgery, or a thromboembolic event), the body naturally increases blood flow and inflammation, so localization is less important, in my experience. I'll never forget a woman who fell off a horse and had painful hairline fractures in five of her vertebrae. She was afraid of lumbar epidural injection, so she took an intravenous treatment from another doctor, and sure enough, within two weeks, she was pain-free. With surgery, I recommend that people wait at least a week because there is no such thing as a completely sterile surgery, and the body's naturally sterilizing inflammation shouldn't be prematurely halted, especially in cases of orthopedic surgery where joints will often have compromised blood flow and are therefore more susceptible to bacterial infection. It would be irresponsible of me to recommend MSC exosomes for strokes or heart attacks, but given the animal models, if I were faced with a decision for myself or a close family member, I would strongly consider them.

The aphorism of the top three most important factors in real estate is something to consider. We know that exosomes are so small that they travel well between cells, in the lymph and blood, and on the surfaces of blood cells. That means that if inhaled nasally, they can travel to the brain via the nerve tracts. Even given intravenously, they can cross the blood-brain barrier. That said, I generally regard location of placement to be important with specific MSK "osis" conditions. I'll never forget treating Doug, the octogenarian runner. We only injected his knee, and some invariably leaked out. He called me four days later to say his thumb felt heavy and slightly inflamed. After a day, the thumb pain resolved for good. It turned out that he had jammed that thumb a decade earlier, and the exosomes had found their way to an old "osis" condition that was amenable to stem cell-based repair.

Nevertheless, if we are interested in treating the brain, per se, the lowest to highest effective delivery methods would likely be intravenous, inhaled nasal, injected nasal, and intrathecal (directly into the spinal fluid at the lumbar spine).

WHAT DOSE AND BRANDS?

Since the serendipitous discovery that the stuff inside the bathwater of a young stem cell culture could cause an old person's stem cells to resume copying, there have been multiple companies that have entered the marketplace. You can get some idea of what brands to choose from a section in the next chapter aimed at providers, but suffice it to say, this is generally not an area that you can have great confidence in understanding.

Why is that? Most people, when filling their car with gasoline, think that the gas will likely be the same in terms of composition, impurities, and basic structure. I suspect that is probably mostly true as well. So, filling your tank comes down to a simple price per gallon, with quality being a secondary factor. When it comes to exosomes, the devil is in the details. <u>Surprisingly, there is no way to reliably compare the billions of one brand to another.</u>

If you find a practice that you are comfortable with and then receive a price quote on a treatment using a defined amount of a specific brand, you can possibly compare apples to apples when contacting another practice. Generally, providers will tolerate but don't love price shoppers, but it might surprise you to discover that one practice charges 2 to 3 times what you originally were quoted. If they are doing a simple intravenous push, I don't really care how nice the office is or how famous their clients are; it is hard to justify that degree of price discrepancy for a simple two-minute procedure.

Truthfully, most practices will use just one brand, insist that their results are better with that brand, and then attempt to compare "100 Billion" of theirs to "15 Billion" of another. As you will learn from the next chapter, these comparisons are largely spurious, but questioning a provider about that will only get you labeled as "difficult."

CHANGE TAKES TIME

If you receive treatment, it may take time to see improvement. Rarely, things improve overnight, but that is usually not the case. Even if pain resolves after treatment, don't forget to limit excessive activity for up to 8 weeks since new collagen is often not the permanent, stronger type. Changes in the macrophages, inflammation, local stem cell behaviors, and rebuilding are processes that take some time. Generally speaking, I've found MSK issues improve by about three weeks but neurological conditions might take six weeks or more to manifest improvements. We can even see changes up to 6 to 8 months after a treatment.

BE REALISTIC BUT HOPEFUL

If you have spent a lifetime acquiring damage to your knee cartilage, for example, it would be unrealistic to expect it to return to your teenage form and function after just one treatment. Because aging and damage are ongoing, it might feel like a "cure" if you have no more pain a few months after a treatment. But you should understand that you may have gone from 20 to 40%, not 20 to 100%. If, or when, your pain recurs, perhaps even years later, your decision might be to do it again rather than say it never worked, but that is just my opinion.

It never hurts to be optimistic about a treatment. If anything, people are not generally good judges of how things used to be, and they gradually adjust to a "new normal." Sometimes, a patient will have no positive changes after two months and give up, but when we reconnect a year later, they might say, "Oh, I haven't felt that pain for at least six months." This happened to me just last week when a referring nurse told me a patient that I had treated was better. I had lost follow-up with her after three months when nothing was happening. When we spoke ten months after her only treatment, she said the injected shoulder stopped hurting a long time before and that the botox treatments for her **torticollis** (painful neck spasms) were spaced out to five months, whereas previously they had been three months apart.

FREQUENCY OF TREATMENTS

Recall the martial artist who did seven treatments despite no pain after two? If you are an elite athlete with the funds, it is unclear whether you can overdo it with exosomes, and the sooner after injury that you use them, the better. One might argue professional football players could benefit from weekly treatments while in season. I once treated a woman with severe burns for eight consecutive weeks, and the repair of her skin was impressive without untoward consequences.

Having said that, for most of us, determining frequency is a matter of results and finances. If you are doing hair restoration, you should commit to at least three treatments. I recommend that if you get no results or feel you are worse from any procedure, don't repeat. If you get completely better, consider repeating after a long interval for maintenance or when the problem starts to recur. If you get somewhat better, consider repeating treatment after a shorter interval.

FINAL THOUGHTS

When a person contacts me, I try my best to ascertain the complete medical history with a focus on the main problems they are facing now. This process can take a few minutes for a young and healthy person, or it could be over an hour for a more complex case. After so many treatments, I feel relatively comfortable telling people what their likelihood of improvement might be, but as with any clinical practice, no one can be certain. I currently practice in five states: California, New York, Florida, Texas, and Hawaii.

In APPENDIX A of this book, I will include descriptions of most of my exosome-related blogs, videos, and webinars, which I've created, complete with their hyperlinks. If you are one of those folks who likes to "binge watch," then you can start with the foundational lectures, nine long-form videos addressing the most frequently asked questions when it comes to exosomes. There is also a plethora of information on unique cases and observations I've made in the first four years of practicing clinical medicine with exosomes. I hope that these resources will prove interesting and potentially helpful to you and those in your close family and social circles. If you know a provider who might want to learn more about providing exosomes in their practice, please refer them to me as well.

To learn more, go to www.rechargebiomedical.com I also have a YouTube channel of "drpark65" with many lectures on exosomes and telomerase activation. In addition, my contact information can be found at www.ovou.me/edwardpark

Chapter 18

NOTES TO PRACTITIONERS

A doctor is not a mechanic.
A car doesn't react with a mechanic,
but a human being does.

—Randa Haines (film director)

In this penultimate chapter, I will be speaking mainly to the healthcare providers, but if you are not one, it might be helpful to lurk and learn just the same. We will talk about legal considerations, medical ethics, lifelong learning, and steps to take if you want to start using exosomes clinically.

PRIMUM NON NOCERE

The section of the Hippocratic oath that should be most cherished is perhaps this phrase, which translates into "*Most importantly, don't harm.*" In the practice of medicine, we must balance not only this **non-maleficence** but also the complimentary medical ethics principles such as **beneficence** (doing good), **autonomy** (independence), and **justice**. At least in the ideal form, a physician or other provider has an ethical obligation to balance these considerations when treating our patients. You are honor-bound to 1) discourage treatments that are likely to cause harm, 2) try to improve their conditions, 3) provide informed consent, and 4) treat patients fairly and equally.

The online provider training course that I created discusses these topics in a lecture entitled "Will I Get in Trouble?" This is a very important thing to consider for anyone. Before we break down the moving parts of answering that question, let's solemnly consider that even when those ethical principles are strained, they must never be ignored despite the confusion and inertia that surrounds the practice of clinical medicine.

Whether you know it or not, there are countless Cochrane Collaboration reports refuting standard medical practice across the board. From continuous fetal monitoring to epidural steroid injections, you can find an expert witness to tell you what you are doing with the best intentions is not "evidence-based." We used to have an expression at the Beth Israel Hospital, where I trained: "Ask two doctors, get four opinions!" The fact is that we often use medications in an "off-label" manner based on science, intuition, and experience. Yet, that is rarely disclosed because these deviations have become the de facto standard of care, and it is not deemed to be relevant to disclose them to the autonomous patient.

For this reason, the practice of medicine demands humility, flexibility, intuition, knowledge, open communication, and courage. Oftentimes, during a surgical residency, we less experienced residents observed more experienced attendings who repeatedly reaped trouble because of pride, inflexibility, dogmatism, bad habits, authoritarianism, and cowardice.

Recently, the FDA lawyer being sued by doctors in front of the 5th Circuit Court of Appeals stated that:

"The agency's ivermectin warnings [were] informational statements, and stressed they are not regulations, they have no legal consequences, and they don't bar doctors from prescribing ivermectin to treat COVID or for any other purpose."

The government's lawyer conceded that 40% of all US prescriptions are used in an off-label fashion and that there is no federal law to ban that practice. That said, they did issue an advisory to state medical and pharmacy boards characterizing ivermectin as primarily a veterinary medicine and did not mention studies suggesting efficacy for the treatment of Coronavirus infections.

Although, as the young people say these days, there are "no lies detected," I don't believe that captures the spirit of the "guidance" that was offered. The doctors using ivermectin were referred for medical board sanction and lost their privileges, and that is why they filed, lost, and then appealed their lawsuit against the FDA for overstepping its authority. The appeal is still pending at the time of this writing, but the FDA defense seems to be "we would never stop doctors from doing their jobs."

Of course, unlike ivermectin, MSC exosomes are not FDA-approved, so their use doesn't even rise to the level of "off-label." There are multiple trials for different conditions, but none have been FDA-approved yet, and as discussed in Chapter 10, they may never be. It is right there on every patient consent that I obtain: "not FDA-approved and NOT standard of care." So why is it that we offer these treatments? Because of **beneficence** and **non-maleficence**. Based on experience, we feel we can help patients without excessive risk of harm. The FDA may send you a warning letter and refer you to a state medical board, but they probably can't regulate your practice of medicine. If anything, they would likely sanction the makers of exosomes.

FTC ACTIONS

The Federal Trade Commission is responsible for regulating commerce and, in particular, advertising. If you offer treatments that are not standard and not FDA-approved, you would do well to limit your advertising of treating specific conditions. An FTC action can result in prolonged legal battles that are difficult to win, although they tend to occur if monetary revenues rise to the level of making financial penalties worthwhile for that agency.

STATE MEDICAL BOARDS

There are many ways to get in trouble with state medical boards. Patients, other practices that feel threatened, or any number of other malicious actors can stir up trouble. There are no sure-fire ways to avoid this, but there are several good principles to adhere to. Avoid high-conflict and unstable patients. If they present with combative demeanors and strong negative feelings about others, then the risk of future conflict might be higher than someone who possesses normal social skills. Once you take on a patient, treat them well. Despite deviation from the standard of care and even despite a bad outcome, the most critical factor in filing a lawsuit or making a medical board complaint would have to be malice. Keep communicating and supporting your patients, and you will lower the risks.

You should carry relevant malpractice insurance that addresses the use of exosomes. Often, they will ask for protocols and scopes of practice. You should also use a comprehensive medical consent form that reiterates the fact that the procedures are not FDA-approved, standard of care, covered by insurance, or guaranteed to help. The consent should also list alternative treatment options, common reactions, and warning signs of complications. The most important considerations for informed consent are that you never attempt procedures that you are not comfortable with, that the patient has uncoerced **autonomy** to decline or modify treatments, and that they are being treated fairly with regard to pricing (**justice**).

SO WHY AM I GOING TO RISK THIS?

Life is full of risk, and it falls on all sides all the time. Even if you don't want to include MSC exosomes in your practice, you should consider using them on yourself. I wouldn't eat at a restaurant that the chef didn't feel comfortable eating at, would you? The first thing I did before opening it up to friends and family was to try MSC exosomes on myself, and even if they become unavailable, I know that many of my problems could be mitigated by their use because I have first-hand experiences.

When you can talk about the same treatment with your own body or your own children, there is an entirely different level of trust that is engendered.

LIFELONG LEARNING

I get it. You're seeing your patients, you're paying your bills, and you don't want to risk anything right now. But let me submit that in a few years, there will be more than the two exosome Covid mRNA products approved by the FDA. We may even see the approval of MSC exosomes for some indication, which may open a crack for off-label homologous use. Also, this revolution in cell biology is just getting started. Since exosomes are fundamental in disease states, their use for the diagnosis of complex metabolic, immunological, and cancer-related conditions is just a matter of time.

You may not want to learn something new, but the newness is coming, whether you like it or not. Take a look at

PubMed now; there are 28,983 articles as of today under the search term "exosomes." This is not a sleepy backwater of obscure pseudoscience and snake oil. This is the fundamental way in which cells, organs, and individuals maintain illness or mitigate it. I think it is a good thing to at least accept that there are interesting discoveries coming down the pike that are related to exosome science.

If you are interested in learning more, I would recommend you start by looking at the last section of the book, where I describe many of the blogs, webinars, and lectures that I've created along the way. If you are interested in using MSC exosomes in your practice, I would recommend taking my online provider training course consisting of more than 12 hours of live, recorded instruction as well as review questions. In this long format, I presented topics and hosted live Q&A about the science, when to use ultrasound, how to treat all the areas mentioned in this book, and the nuts and bolts of starting your practice, including protocols for nasal injection, patient consents, and aftercare instructions. The course can be found at www.rechargebiomedical.com/courses

CHOOSING YOUR BRAND

Again, the rule of thumb would be *caveat emptor*. Since 2018, there have been several companies that have come and gone, but the majority have been flourishing by offering what they describe as more for less. At the time of this writing, I can say a few things with absolute certainty about exosome manufacturers.

- You don't know how they are operating. When I get calls from the sales representatives, but even founders and chief scientific officers, they either don't know or don't share what they are doing to make the exosomes.

- More donors always mean more opportunities for infectious and toxic risks, despite some companies' illogical assertions to the contrary. If they don't test their product for sterility and dozens of known pathogens and toxins, then run away

- If the companies don't validate the canonical (accepted) surface markers of CD9, CD63, and CD81, they can't be sure they are providing actual MSC exosomes.

- Freeze-dried products do not approach anywhere near the true biological viability of those that are cryopreserved and should only be used topically.

- If they don't open their exosomes with detergent and then analyze RNA content, they can't really know the potency nor the contents of the alleged exosomes.

- Every company relies on an optical particle counting device known as a Nanocyte, which you adjust by turning your wrist to read from zero to trillions of particles per milliliter, that you then call "exosomes". Particle counts are thus subject to misrepresentation, whether it be from pure distilled water or from a true sample of resuspended exosomes.

In general, a lab should offer a site visit. Please go and visit and see whether they have the physical plant, staffing, and professional equipment to maintain quality control. If you can get a science officer on the phone, do that. Ask questions about sourcing, how frequently they renew the cell lines, whether they do infectious disease and toxin testing, whether they have been FDA site inspected, and what quality control measures are in place.

Once you select a brand, be prepared to pivot. Be honest about the efficacy, and if you have untoward reactions, always report this to the manufacturer and record the lot number and details for your records. True MSC exosomes suspended in normal saline should be clear, odorless, and salty to the taste.

If you find a brand that works, don't become married to it. Price is not the only consideration, and there may be other brands that are better. I would hate to see your practice use one brand for themselves and their family but a cheaper brand for patients. I have only used one brand these four years because I've never had a weak, cloudy, contaminated, recalled, or unsafe batch due to quarantine, inspection, continuous frozen storage, and sterile techniques using only one patient per vial.

Sadly, providers are at the mercy of manufacturers who have many incentives to misrepresent, exaggerate, cut corners, and make sales. No amount of profit margin could ever justify using a product of dubious quality. Trust your results and intuition and meticulously record lot numbers and maintain your exosomes sealed, frozen, and within the expiration dates. Don't let your ego, confirmation bias, and profit margin dictate what product to use; aim to make less and help more so that patients are happy and feel well-treated. The online provider course talks about managing patient expectations in addition to providing practical tips and pearls. All my clinical forms are also available for download and customization. For more information and reviews from people who took the course, see Appendix B.

In the end, we are all autonomous people trying to help autonomous patients come to a fair and informed decision about a new and promising technology that is exactly homologous to what works best in our bodies, from birth to death. If we are of the constant improvement mindset and we put **beneficence** and **non-maleficence** at the forefront of all our decisions, we hope that only the very best outcomes will ensue. Don't hesitate to contact me at www.ovou.me/edwardpark or connect with me at www.rechargebiomedical.com if you have any questions that I can help you with. I have treated myself at least 25 times, not including eye drops; my mother has received 34 treatments, and even my sons have had numerous treatments when the need arises. There is something very remarkable happening with this revolution in medicine and I hope that you can also help people by becoming a part of it.

Chapter 19

CONCLUSIONS

The future cannot be predicted,
but futures can be invented.

—Dennis Gabor
(physicist and author of *Inventing the Future*)

With the exception of neurobiology, the general interest in exosomes only started to expand around 2010. The professional organization known as the ISEV (International Society for Extracellular Vesicles) only started in 2011. This book is being written in 2023, only a dozen years into this revolution. Yet somehow, thanks to the synchronicity of some friends in need, a brilliant stem cell scientist found out that the bathwater, and not the stem cell babies, was where the magic was really to be found.

I had been studying exosomes with some PhDs and MDs prior to hearing the remarkable story of the neurologist with the motorcycle accident in 2018. From my growing clinical experiences, I have found that many, but not all, conditions can often be positively impacted by their usage.

This revolution has not yet even begun. The majority of bench science still ignores the primary mode of cell-to-cell communication that is implicated by this exosome paradigm. They lack the knowledge, equipment, training, and credence to embrace new ideas, and the old ways are sufficient to get grants, publish papers, and maintain tenure or employment.

To be frank, if we didn't have ears to hear, minds to enjoy, and legs to dance to an imperceptible form of music, why would we bother? Because cells that dictate our well-being and our very mortality are the ones who are making and dancing to this music. The understanding of music theories underlying these dances is where the great "cures" of the future will come from.

ALREADY PROVEN

The ability to create custom exosomes with specific mRNA cargo has been proven with the deployment of Covid vaccines, although the use of their artificial lipid nanoparticle bilayers is controversial. It remains to be seen whether history will validate this method of disease prophylaxis but we already know there are many conditions that could benefit from replacing missing genes for patients with rare genetic disorders.

Imagine having a rare genetic disease and all you need to do is replace that mRNA or protein with an affordable monthly exosome injection. Imagine having pancreatic cancer and treating it with the seriousness of cutting off a skin cancer from your back because an off-the-shelf exosome with four mRNA oncogenes is associated with a 99% cure rate.

We may never master the subtle notes, scales, chords, harmonies, and motifs of cell biology, but someday, perhaps exosomes from folks with resolving serious illness will be readily available just as we have intravenous immunoglobulins or packed red blood cells for use currently.

Ideally, since the technology exists to print out any mRNA we want, we could someday have a world where damaged cells could be screened for gene deletions, and then the missing genes could be supplemented with bespoke exosomes, all while you wait.

If we consider the depletion and exhaustion of the immune system to be a foundation of aging, we could also imagine a day when immune stem cells are harvested, expanded, and reintroduced to restore our immune resilience. The mastery of stem cell isolation, cryopreservation and banking, and purposeful differentiation is still in its infancy but promises to unlock the secrets of the *Trimurti* for the benefit of all life on earth.

I'm sorry if the good news presented in this book somehow represents a threat. I encourage you to look up the citations, check out the hyperlinks to my work, and do independent research to verify that what I'm telling you is accurate. Please forgive me if my explanations were too complicated or hard to follow. It was a true pleasure to write this book for you, and I hope that, in some way, it may have improved your life and offered you some hope. I appreciate your attention, hard work, and willingness to learn. Thank you so much, and please don't hesitate to contact me via www.ovou.me/edwardpark if you have any questions.

ACKNOWLEDGEMENTS

There is a good reason they call it practicing, and not mastering, medicine. Practitioners are constantly improving discernment, knowledge of science, clinical expertise, and wisdom by simply listening, guessing, trying, and honestly assessing what works and what doesn't.

For all those patients who read, understood, and yet still signed a consent reading, "This is not FDA-approved, not standard of care, and not guaranteed to work," I owe the highest debt of gratitude. Thanks to their intuition, faith, and courage, we were able to improve lives in most cases, and the feeling of helping someone who is suffering is one that makes life worth living.

I also want to thank my mother, Young Joo Park, who, after 34 injections and counting, has become a wonderful source of clinical experience and one of my biggest fans.

Finally, I want to thank scientists who are constantly increasing human knowledge about biology, the most complex subject of them all. I have been privileged to not only teach, but also to learn from some of the most courageous, innovative, and knowledgeable people. In many cases, those folks were not MDs or DOs, but NPs, NDs, chiropractors, and even patients themselves.

We are all in this together, and together, we will someday mitigate diseases of stem cell degradation and depletion that future generations will only read about in books.

APPENDIX A

ONLINE EDUCATIONAL MATERIALS

FOUNDATIONAL LECTURES

What is an Exosome? www.tinyurl.com/exosomes1	In this 26-minute video Dr. Ed Park of Recharge Biomedical explains what exosomes are and why conditions like cancer and aging may be the direct result of the ecology that exosomes are creating.
What is aging? www.tinyurl.com/exosomes2	In this 31-minute video, Dr. Ed Park explains aging and how exosomes may be the cause and part of the solution for it.
Parabiosis www.tinyurl.com/exosomes3	In this 18-minute video, Dr. Ed Park explains parabiosis, or the mixing of young and old organisms
Cancer and exosomes www.tinyurl.com/exosomes4	In this 18-minute video, Dr. Ed Park explains a new paradigm for cancer in which it is not rare, hereditary, nor incurable. The role that exosomes play in cancer ecology is discussed.
Regenerative Joint therapies www.tinyurl.com/exosomes5	In this 38-minute video, Dr. Ed Park explains of how attempts at helping the body repair have evolved over time.

Are all exosomes created equal? www.tinyurl.com/ exosomes6	In this 21-minute video, Dr. Ed Park explains that exosomes are all different. The cells are musicians that put messenger RNA, blocking RNA, and proteins into bespoke little packages that work like songs to make other cells "dance".
The FDA www.tinyurl.com/ exosomes7	In this 23-minute video, Dr. Ed Park explains how the FDA works. I explain the "minimally- altered" standard that regulates use of stem cells in the United States.
What are the risks of exosomes? www.tinyurl.com/ exosomes8	In this 17-minute video, Dr. Ed Park explains the possible risks associated with exosomes.
Dr. Park's approach to exosomes www.tinyurl.com/ exosomes9	In this 27-minute video, Dr. Ed Park of Recharge Biomedical reviews his approach to exosomes in the context of age mitigation, safety, efficacy, cost, and the patient-physician relationship.

EXOSOME BLOGS

Exosomes 1: The Journey Begins https://tinyurl.com/exoblog1	Last week, I opened the practice to friends and longstanding patients. I will share some notes about my observations
Exosomes 2: Not inert https://tinyurl.com/exoblog2	Today is day 15 after injection and for the first time in a long time, this 80-yo completed his 5.8mile run without stopping to walk due to knee pain. He is very happy!
Exosomes 3: Brain and Neck trauma https://tinyurl.com/exoblog3	It is possible that the anti-inflammatory nature of the exosomes helped to relax the muscles, allowing for resolution of the whiplash and muscle spasms that were producing subluxation
Exosomes 4: Back on the treadmill again https://tinyurl.com/exoblog4	It appears that the benefits of tendon injection are gradual and continuous and are better at four weeks than at two weeks
Exosomes 5: Clinical Medicine in Bittersweet https://tinyurl.com/exoblog5	"we don't see things as they are, we see things as we are." Evidence-based medicine and the doctrines of standard empiricism offer a structure for analyzing medical decision making but are not sufficient
Exosomes 6: Healing Takes Time https://tinyurl.com/exoblog6	A patient whom I treated sent a 3-minute video of talk show host, Joe Rogan, explaining how he feels exosomes fixed his shoulder labrum tear

Exosomes 7: Nerve Pain Gone https://tinyurl.com/exoblog7	Within 24 hours, The pain she had endured for four years was completely gone and has remained gone for over a week
Exosomes 8: Disinformation or Bad Science https://tinyurl.com/exoblog8	Unless you gently dissolve the lipid bilayers of the exosomes with detergent that doesn't also destroy the contents, you can't know what's inside.
Exosomes 10: Interviews with exosomes experts https://tinyurl.com/exoblog10	To watch these seven related videos interviewing experts in regenerative medicine with a focus on exosomes and their many uses
Exosomes 11: Deb B's knees are improving https://tinyurl.com/exoblog11	This week's blog is a video posting about my patient, 65-yo Deb B. She received exosome therapy two and a half weeks ago and from the first moments of injection, she has felt much better.
Exosomes 12: 80yo Doug runs 121 miles in 6 days https://tinyurl.com/exoblog12	This week's blog is about 80-yo Doug. Since exosome injection in March, he has been running...a lot. Just a few weeks ago, he ran 121miles in 6 days.
Exosomes 13: Microneedling my Mom with exosomes https://tinyurl.com/exoblog13	Mom claims the face is smoother, wrinkles faded, and pores are smaller just four days after microneedling with exosomes
Exosomes 14: The shoulder https://tinyurl.com/exoblog14	"I went to the gym to test my bad shoulder that injected. It is now better than my good shoulder with at least 90% improvement so far"

Exosomes 15: Face Blindness https://tinyurl.com/exoblog15	I'm happy to report that her face blindness has seen a 30% improvement which has brought her to the point of not being nervous in social situations
Exosomes 16: Lectures in Hawaii https://tinyurl.com/exoblog16	I have posted two lectures given in Hawaii. The first is a general lecture and the second is about clinical applications of exosomes
Exosomes 17: Reading is "fun"damental https://tinyurl.com/exoblog17	If you are someone who once enjoyed reading but now find it hard to concentrate, you may want to also consider nasal exosome therapy
Exosomes 18: Dental health improved https://tinyurl.com/exoblog18	For those of you who are battling the gradual loss of teeth and dental health, perhaps exosomes therapy can offer some relief
Exosomes 19: Chakra Balancing https://tinyurl.com/exoblog19	In the traditional Hindu religion, they speak of Chakras which are subtle energy "wheels" of a mixed literal and allegorical nature
Exosomes 20: Seborrheic Dermatitis https://tinyurl.com/exoblog20	This blog is about a case of seborrheic dermatitis that improved after exosomes given with microneedling.
Exosomes 21: Bias in unavoidable https://tinyurl.com/exoblog21	The ability to be a reliable historian and judge of any changes after exosome therapy is a challenge for nearly everyone.

Exosomes 22: Is there really no such thing as bad press? https://tinyurl.com/exoblog22	One year ago, few people had heard of exosomes and everyone was a friend; 12 months later gossip and slander are as plentiful as beach balls and t-shirts from cannons at a summer music festival.
Exosomes 23: Stasis Dermatitis https://tinyurl.com/exoblog23	It appears that exosomes from young exosomes may have helped the venous stasis and resultant dermatitis in this patient
Exosomes 24: How long do exosomes last? https://tinyurl.com/exoblog24	If you wash an undamaged car really well and then garage it in a dustless vacuum chamber away from the sun, the car will stay pretty clean for a really long time
Exosomes 25: Knee treatments https://tinyurl.com/exoblog25	Of all the treatments I do, I believe exosome treatment of knees are one the most effective.
Exosomes 26: The Placebo Effect https://tinyurl.com/exoblog26	People would like to believe that the placebo effect can repair many things, but the truth is that faith healing comes from belief in real results
Exosomes 27: Soft signs of Exosomes Actions https://tinyurl.com/exoblog27	I suppose you could say we experience a force in both a Newtonian sense and in the Star Wars sense!
Exosomes 28: Varicose Veins https://tinyurl.com/exoblog28	Within ten days of exosome therapy, this 48-yo's varicose veins disappeared

Exosomes 29: Are exosomes "smart?" https://tinyurl.com/exoblog29	Most likely, the exosomes dock and release their contents rather indiscriminately into many types of cells.
Exosomes 31: Leg Swelling https://tinyurl.com/exoblog31	I present some cases of resolution of leg swelling after use of exosomes and will explain what could be causing this improvement.
Exosomes 32: Nerve Regeneration https://tinyurl.com/exoblog32	Within 12 hours, the sensation returned in the first two fingers of his left hands and he experienced improvement in fine touch in the soles of his feet
Exosomes 33: Reversal of Menopause in a 71yo woman https://tinyurl.com/exoblog33	I want to describe a fascinating case of resumption of menstruation in a 71-yo woman
Exosomes 34: Double Vision https://tinyurl.com/exoblog34	About 7 weeks ago, I gave 5B IV MSC exosomes to a 76-yo woman.Since then, she states the double vision has resolved
Exosomes 35: Cold Hands and Feet https://tinyurl.com/exoblog35	Exosomes may help with chronically cold feet by assisting circulation
Exosomes 36: Tinnitus https://tinyurl.com/exoblog36	This blog is a case report of a patient who experienced dramatic improvement in her tinnitus after exosome injection.

Exosomes 37: The First Year's Results https://tinyurl.com/exoblog37	In this blog, I would like to honestly and comprehensively review my first year of clinical use of exosomes.
Exosomes 38: Bell's (Facial nerve) Palsy https://tinyurl.com/exoblog38	This brief blog is a summary of an interesting case of Bell's Palsy that improved after MSC exosome injection
Exosomes 39: The delayed reactions https://tinyurl.com/exoblog39	I describe instances where the improvements after exosomes took months to manifest
Exosomes 40: Traumatic Brain Injury https://tinyurl.com/exoblog40	A man with a history of traumatic brain injury had improvements in tinnitus, hyperacusis, and facial neuralgia
Exosomes 41: Leg neuropathy https://tinyurl.com/exoblog41	75-yo Bob had a five-year history of idiopathic lower leg neuropathy. Exosome injections were associated with significant improvements.
Exosomes 42: Facial Rejuvenation https://tinyurl.com/exoblog42	47-yo woman claims her face looks younger after a microneedling treatment with exosomes
Exosomes 44: Long Covid https://tinyurl.com/exoblog44	51-yo woman with "Covid brain" describes her symptom improvements after exosome treatments

EXOSOME WEBINARS

Exosome Webinar 1: What are Exosomes https://tinyurl.com/exoweb1	Dr. Ed Park explains what exosomes are. Run time 24 minutes
Exosome Webinar 2: "Back Pain" https://tinyurl.com/exoweb2	Dr. Ed Park explains back pain and its common causes. Can exosomes help? We speak to a patient who believes they did
Exosomes Webinar 3: The Shoulders https://tinyurl.com/exoweb3	Dr. Ed Park of Recharge Biomedical explains the shoulders, their common problems, and typical treatments. He also describes his experiences using exosomes in the areas.
Exosomes Webinar 4: The knees https://tinyurl.com/exoweb4	Dr. Ed Park of Recharge Biomedical explains knee anatomy and function. He describes common knee problems and their treatments.
Exosomes Webinar 5: Gout https://tinyurl.com/exoweb5	Dr. Ed Park of Recharge Biomedical explains what causes Gout and how it is typically managed.
Exosomes Webinar 6: The Hips https://tinyurl.com/exoweb6	Dr. Ed Park of Recharge Biomedical explains hip anatomy and function. Are you hip to how important the hips are?
Exosomes Webinar 7: Tendons https://tinyurl.com/exoweb7	Dr. Ed Park of Recharge Biomedical tendons and how they repair. He presents several cases of exosome use in tendinopathy

Exosomes Webinar 8: Menopause https://tinyurl.com/ exoweb8	Dr. Ed Park of Recharge Biomedical explains current thinking on menopause and presents a remarkable case of a 73yo who resumed menstruation
Exosomes Webinar 9: Leaky Gut https://tinyurl.com/ exoweb9	Dr. Ed Park of Recharge Biomedical presents a remarkable case of clinical improvements that may represent improvement in leaky gut syndrome. Is leaky gut a real thing?
Exosomes Webinar 10: Stasis Dermatitis https:/tinyurl.com/ exoweb10	Dr. Ed Park of Recharge Biomedical explains the common conditions of stasis dermatitis and leg swelling. He presents several cases of improvement after use of MSC exosomes
Exosomes Webinar 11: Nerve Generation https://tinyurl.com/ exoweb11	Dr. Ed Park of Recharge Biomedical presents three cases of nerve regeneration after use of MSC exosomes. How do nerves regenerate?
Exosomes Webinar 12: Stroke Rehab https://tinyurl.com/ exoweb12	Dr. Ed Park of Recharge Biomedical explains strokes and presents two cases of symptom improvement after exosome use
Exosomes Webinar 13: Dental Problems https://tinyurl.com/ exoweb13	Dr. Ed Park of Recharge Biomedical explains dental problems and presents two cases where exosomes may have been helpful
Exosomes Webinar 14: Erectile dysfunction https://tinyurl.com/ exoweb14	Dr. Ed Park of Recharge Biomedical explains what causes Erectile Dysfunction and the methods commonly used to treat it.

Exosomes Webinar 15: FAQs https://tinyurl.com/exoweb15	Dr. Ed Park of Recharge Biomedical addresses FAQs about exosome treatments. How are they different from stem cells? Are they FDA-approved? How much does it cost? What are his results?
Exosomes Webinar 16: Acne https://tinyurl.com/exoweb16	Dr. Ed Park of Recharge Biomedical explains acne: what causes it, how to prevent and treat it, and how exosomes might have helped one case improve
Exosomes Webinar 17: Tinnitus https://tinyurl.com/exoweb17	Dr. Ed Park of Recharge Biomedical explains tinnitus, or ringing in the ears.
Exosomes Webinar 18: Face Blindness https://tinyurl.com/exoweb18	Dr. Ed Park of Recharge Biomedical explains face blindness, or prosopagnosia, which affects about one in fifty people.
Exosomes Webinar 19: Vision https://tinyurl.com/exoweb19	Dr. Ed Park of Recharge Biomedical explains vision and describes two cases of improvement after exosomes.
Exosomes Webinar 20: Hair Loss https://tinyurl.com/exoweb20	Dr. Ed Park of Recharge Biomedical explains hair growth and loss. Three cases of exosome use with microneedling are presented
Exosomes Webinar 21: Autoimmunity https://tinyurl.com/exoweb21	Dr. Ed Park of Recharge Biomedical explains autoimmunity by way of explaining our immune systems.

Exosomes Webinar 22: Aging https://tinyurl.com/exoweb22	Dr. Ed Park of Recharge Biomedical explains his theory of aging. How could exosomes help mitigate the challenges of aging?
Exosomes Webinar 23: MSCs https://tinyurl.com/exoweb23	Dr. Ed Park of Recharge Biomedical tries to explain what Mesenchymal Stem Cells are and why their exosomes are so special
Exosomes Webinar 24: Comparing exosomes https://tinyurl.com/exoweb24	Dr. Ed Park of Recharge Biomedical explains how exosomes are made and validated. Dr. Duncan Ross interviewed
Exosomes Webinar 25: Repeat Injections https://tinyurl.com/exoweb25	Why do 50% of our patients choose to repeat treatments?
Exosomes Webinar 26: Best Cases https://tinyurl.com/exoweb26	Dr. Park presents some the best results after exosome use
Exosomes Webinar 27: Unhappy Patients https://tinyurl.com/exoweb27	Dr. Ed Park explains why some patients are unhappy after exosome use. A live webinar with actual patients calling in
Exosomes Webinar 28: Science of Exosomes https://tinyurl.com/exoweb28	Dr. Ed Park of Recharge Biomedical explains of the basics of exosome science
Exosomes Webinar 29: ICYMI https://tinyurl.com/exoweb29	Dr. Ed Park reviews the educational materials he has been making regarding exosomes

Exosomes Webinar 30: Injection techniques https://tinyurl.com/exoweb30	Dr. Ed Park explains some common injection techniques
Exosomes Webinar 31: Stem Cells vs. Exosomes https://tinyurl.com/exoweb31	Dr. Ed Park explains the differences between stem cell and exosome therapy
Exosomes Webinar 32: Ask me Anything https://tinyurl.com/exoweb32	Dr. Ed Park answers your questions live. Topics include how they go where they're needed, what is the spinal versus epidural injection, and whether pets are telepathic
Exosomes Webinar 33: What is in exosomes? https://tinyurl.com/exoweb33	Dr. Ed Park does a live webinar explaining what is in MSC exosomes and how they may be assisting in regeneration and anti- inflammation.

APPENDIX B

ONLINE PROVIDER TRAINING COURSE

I created an online advanced provider self-directed training course. It is 20 lessons running 12 hours and has 256 review questions. Topics include: efficacy, legal issues, brands, pricing, science, patient satisfaction, ultrasound, MSK use, the nervous system, facial rejuvenation, sexual health, and countless practice pearls.

"I loved the Exosome Masterclass series! Dr. Park's teaching method ensures your success in mastering this complex topic. His uniquely personable style makes the material come alive, making it easier to grasp and recall. There are also an ongoing self-quizzes as you go through the various classes, again, facilitating retention. And you end up with a thorough knowledge of the various aspects of using exosomes in clinical practice. I highly recommend this course!"

Hyla Cass MD
Former Professor of Psychiatry
UCLA School of Medicine
Diplomate American Board of Integrative
Holistic Medicine (ABIHM)

"I am completely grateful to Dr. Park for putting his course on exosomes together. I was intrigued by the possibilities of introducing them into my longevity practice and his educational series has given me the foundation of understanding I needed to begin using them. The course provides in depth basic science with myriad examples of clinical applications so that one can approach using exosomes with patients with an appropriate blend of optimism, excitement, and tempered caution."

Kenneth R. Kafka, MD
Double board certified in Internal Medicine
and Anti-aging Medicine

"I highly recommend this to anyone wanting to learn more about exosomes and the emerging field of use for them. His compassion and desire to help shows forth in the way he interacts, teaches, and makes himself available. This class was excellent, and I am grateful that I was able to participate."

Jodi Repko, ARNP- FNP-BC
Functional, Integrative, and
Emergency Medicine

To sign up for the course:

https://www.rechargebiomedical.com/courses/
clinical-use-of-msc-exosomes/

To watch a video about the class:

https://tinyurl.com/exosomeclass

ENDNOTES

Chapter 1: A WHOLE NEW PARADIGM

1. James R. Edgar. https://commons.wikimedia.org/wiki/
    File:A_transmission_electron_micrograph_of_an_
    Epstein%E2%80%93Barr_virus-transformed_B_cell_
    displaying_newly_expelled_exosomes_at_the_plasma_
    membrane.jpg

2. https://youtu.be/f1x9lgX8GaE?feature=shared&t=4298

Chapter 2: A CRASH COURSE IN CELL BIOLOGY

1. T Ushijima, N Watanabe, E Okochi, A Kaneda, T Sugimura, K Miyamoto. Fidelity of the Methylation Pattern and Its Variation in the Genome. *Genome Res.* 2003. 13: 868-874.

2. LFZ Batista, MF Pech, FL Zhong, HN Nguyen, KT Xie, AJ Zaug, SM Crary, JK Choi, V Sebastiano, A Cherry, N Giri, M Wernig, BP Alter, TR Cech, SA Savage, RA Reijo Pera, SE Artandi. Telomere shortening and loss of self-renewal in dyskeratosis congenita induced pluripotent stem cells. *Nature.* 2011 May 22;474(7351):399-402.

3. Yi Jin, Min Xu, Hai Zhu, Chen Dong, Juan Ji, Yake Liu, Aidong Deng, Zhifeng Gu. Therapeutic effects of bone marrow mesenchymal stem cells-derived exosomes on osteoarthritis. *J Cell Mol Med.* 2021 Oct; 25(19): 9281–9294.

4. SN Catlin, L Busque, RE Gale, P Guttorp, JL Abkowitz. 2011. The replication rate of human hematopoietic stem cells in vivo. *Blood.* 117:4460–4466.

5. H Holstege, W Pfeiffer, D Sie, M Hulsman, T Nicholas, C Lee, T Ross, J Lin, M Miller, B Ylstra, H Meijers-Heijboer, MH Brugman, F Staal, G Holstege, M Reinders, T Harkins, S Levy, E Sistermans. Somatic mutations found in the healthy blood compartment of a 115-yr-old woman demonstrate oligoclonal hematopoiesis. *Genome Research*. 2014 May;24(5):733-42

6. E. Eggenhofer, V. Benseler, A. Kroemer, F. C. Popp, E. K. Geissler, H. J. Schlitt, C. C. Baan, M. H. Dahlke, and M. J. Hoogduijn. Mesenchymal stem cells are short-lived and do not migrate beyond the lungs after intravenous infusion. *Front Immunol*. 2012; 3: 297.

7. https://twitter.com/BWHPath/status/1339617139083235329

8. M Secco, E Zucconi, N Vieira, L Fogaça, A Cerqueira, M Carvalho, T Jazedje, O Okamoto, A Muotri, M Zatz. Mesenchymal stem cells from umbilical cord: do not discard the cord! *Neuromuscul Disorders*. 2008 Jan;18(1):17-8.

9. https://docs.justia.com/cases/federal/district-courts/california/cacdce/5:2018cv01005/709831/191

10. A Viader, L Chang, T Fahrner, R Nagarajan, J Milbrandt. MicroRNAs modulate Schwann cell response to nerve injury by reinforcing transcriptional silencing of dedifferentiation-related genes. *The Journal of Neuroscience*. 2011 Nov 30;31(48):17358-69.

11. M Sulak, L Fong, K Mika, S Chigurupati, L Yon, N Mongan, RD Emes, VJ Lynch. TP53 copy number expansion is associated with the evolution of increased body size and an enhanced DNA damage response in elephants. *eLife*. 2016; 5: e11994.

Chapter 4: THE MESENCHYMAL STEM CELL (MSC)

1. S Lamouille, J Xu, R Derynck. Molecular mechanisms of epithelial–mesenchymal transition. *Nat Rev Mol Cell Biol*. 2014 Mar; 15(3): 178–196.

2. M Dominici, K Le Blanc, I Mueller, I Slaper-Cortenbach, Fc Marini, Ds Krause, Rj Deans, A Keating, Dj Prockop, Em Horwitz. Minimal criteria for defining multipotent mesenchymal stromal cells. The International Society for Cellular Therapy position statement. *Cytotherapy*. 2006;8(4):315-7.

3. H Suila. "Glycobiological insights in characterization and targeting of umbilical cord blood derived stem cells". (Academic Dissertation, Univ of Helsinki, 2014), p15.

4. Arnold I Caplan. Mesenchymal Stem Cells: Time to Change the Name! Stem Cells *Transl Med*. 2017 Jun;6(6):1445-1451.

Chapter 5: A BRIEF HISTORY OF REGENERATIVE MEDICINE

1. https://tinyurl.com/exoblog8

2. T McAlindon, M LaValley, W Harvey, L Price, J Driban, M Zhang, R Ward. Effect of Intra-articular Triamcinolone vs Saline on Knee Cartilage Volume and Pain in Patients With Knee Osteoarthritis. *JAMA*. 2017 May 16; 317(19): 1967–1975.

3. Andrew W Nichols. Complications associated with the use of corticosteroids in the treatment of athletic injuries. *Clin J Sport Med*. 2005 Sep;15(5):370-5.

4. https://www.cochrane.org/CD001824/BACK_injection-therapy-for-subacute-and-chronic-low-back-pain

5. https://www.fda.gov/drugs/drug-safety-and-availability/fda-drug-safety-communication-fda-requires-label-changes-warn-rare-serious-neurologic-problems-after

6. Y Jin, M Xu, H Zhu, C Dong, J Ji, Y Liu, A Deng, Z Gu. Therapeutic effects of bone marrow mesenchymal stem cells-derived exosomes on osteoarthritis. *J Cell Mol Med*. 2021 Oct; 25(19): 9281-9294.

7. J Staal, R de Bie, H de Vet, J Hildebrandt, P Nelemans. Injection therapy for subacute and chronic low-back pain. *Cochrane library*. 16 July 2008.

8. H Heijnen, A Schiel, R Fijnheer, H Geuze, J Sixma. Activated Platelets Release Two Types of Membrane Vesicles: Microvesicles by Surface Shedding and Exosomes Derived From Exocytosis of Multivesicular Bodies and alpha-Granules. *Blood* (1999) 94 (11): 3791–3799.

9. E Eggenhofer, V Benseler, A Kroemer, FC Popp, EK Geissler, HJ Schlitt, CC Baan, MH Dahlke, MJ Hoogduijn. Mesenchymal stem cells are short-lived and do not migrate beyond the lungs after intravenous infusion. *Front Immunol*. 2012; 3: 297.

10. BC Tee, Z Sun. Xenogeneic mesenchymal stem cell transplantation for mandibular defect regeneration. *XENOTRANSPLANTATION*. 06 July 2020

11. M Xie, S Zhang, F Dong, Q Zhang, J Wang, C Wang, C Zhu, S Zhang, B Luo, P Wu, H Ema. Granulocyte colony-stimulating factor directly acts on mouse lymphoid-biased but not myeloid-biased hematopoietic stem cells. *Haematologica* 2021 Volume 106(6):1647-1658.

12. J Kim, NK Kim, SR Park, BH Choi. GM-CSF Enhances Mobilization of Bone Marrow Mesenchymal Stem Cells via a CXCR4-Medicated Mechanism. *Tissue Eng Regen Med*. 2019 Feb; 16(1): 59–68

13. C Qiu, Q Xie, D Zhang, Q Chen, J Hu, L Xu. GM-CSF Induces Cyclin D1 Expression and Proliferation of Endothelial Progenitor Cells via PI3K and MAPK Signaling.*Cellular Physiology and Biochemistry*. (2014) 33 (3): 784–795.

14. Aaron Brown. *Scientific Principles of Adipose Stem Cells*. Academic Press (2021). Chapter 4:57-80

15. B Vezzani, I Shaw, H Lesme, L Yong, N Khan, C Tremolada, B Péault. Higher Pericyte Content and Secretory Activity of Microfragmented Human Adipose Tissue Compared to Enzymatically Derived Stromal Vascular Fraction. *STEM CELLS TRANSLATIONAL MEDICINE*. 2018;7:876–886.

16. HP Lorenz, NS Adzic. Scarless Skin Wound Repair in the Fetus. *Fetal Medicine [Special Issue].West J Med* 1993; 159:350-355).

17. X Pu, S Ma, Y Gao, T Xu, P Chang, L Dong. Mesenchymal Stem Cell-Derived Exosomes: Biological Function and Their Therapeutic Potential in Radiation Damage. *Cells*, 30 Dec 2020, 10(1): E42.

Chapter 6: THE WORLD OF EXOSOMES

1. L Muller, CS Hong, DB Stolz, SC Watkins, TL Whiteside. Isolation of Biologically-Active Exosomes from Human Plasma. *J Immunol Methods*. 2014 September ; 411: 55–65

2. J Xu, K Liao, W Zhou. Exosomes Regulate the Transformation of Cancer Cells in Cancer Stem Cell Homeostasis. *Stem Cells Int*. 2018 Sep 23.

3. Q Zhang, Y Qu, Q Zhang, F Li, B Li, Z Li, Y Dong, L Lu, X Cai. Exosomes derived from hepatitis B virus-infected hepatocytes promote liver fibrosis via miR-222/TFRC axis. *Cell Biol Toxicol*. 2023 Apr;39(2):467-48

4. V Thongboonkerd, R Kanlaya. The divergent roles of exosomes in kidney diseases: Pathogenesis, diagnostics, prognostics and therapeutics. *Int J Biochem Cell Biol*. 2022 Aug;149:106262.

Chapter 7: HOW TO BE IMMORTAL

1. W Jürgens-Wemheuer, A Wrede, Walter Schulz-Schaeffer. Defining the Prion Type of Fatal Familial Insomnia. *Pathogens*. 2021 Oct; 10(10): 1293.

2. T Ushijima, N Watanabe, E Okochi, A Kaneda, T Sugimura, K Miyamoto. Fidelity of the Methylation Pattern and Its Variation in the Genome. *Genome Res*. 2003. 13: 868-874.

Chapter 8: OSIS IN THE BODY

1. AW Nichols. Complications associated with the use of corticosteroids in the treatment of athletic injuries. *Clin J Sport Med.* 2005 Sep;15(5):370-5

2. R Pignolo, RK Suda, EA Mcmillan, J Shen, SH Lee, YW Choi, AC Wright, FB Johnson. Defects in telomere maintenance molecules impair osteoblast differentiation and promote osteoporosis. *Aging Cell* (2008) 7, pp 23–31.

3. Y Jin, M Xu, H Zhu, C Dong, J Ji, Y Liu, A Deng, Z Gu. Therapeutic effects of bone marrow mesenchymal stem cells-derived exosomes on osteoarthritis. *J Cell Mol Med.* 2021 Oct; 25(19): 9281-9294.

Chapter 9: THE IMMUNE SYSTEM

1. H Holstege, W Pfeiffer, D Sie, M Hulsman, T Nicholas, C Lee, T Ross, J Lin, M Miller, B Ylstra, H Meijers-Heijboer, MH Brugman, F Staal, G Holstege, M Reinders, T Harkins, S Levy, E Sistermans. Somatic mutations found in the healthy blood compartment of a 115-yr-old woman demonstrate oligoclonal hematopoiesis. *Genome Research.* 2014 May;24(5):733-42.

2. I Stelmach, M Bobrowska-Korzeniowska, K Smejda, P Majak, J Jerzynska, W Stelmach, K Polańska, W Sobala, J Krysicka, W Hanke. Risk factors for the development of atopic dermatitis and early wheeze. *Allergy Asthma Proc.* 2014 Sep-Oct;35(5):382-9.

3. G Singaravelu, CB Harley, JM Raffaele, P Sudhakaran, A Suram. Double-Blind, Placebo-Controlled, Randomized Clinical Trial Demonstrates Telomerase Activator TA-65 Decreases Immunosenescent CD8+CD28- T Cells in Humans. *OBM Geriatrics* **2021**, Volume 5, Issue 2.

4. https://www.aacr.org/about-the-aacr/newsroom/news-releases/hiv-positive-patients-with-cancer-may-have-accelerated-biological-aging/

5. https://commons.wikimedia.org/wiki/File:Blausen_0425_Formed_Elements.png

6. Adapted from: Seita J, Weissman IL. Hematopoietic stem cell: self-renewal versus differentiation [J]. Wiley *Interdiscip Rev Syst Biol Med*. 2010, 2(6):640–53)

7. H Zhong, RY Lu, Y Wang. Neutrophil extracellular traps in fungal infections: A seesaw battle in hosts. *Front Immunol*. 2022 Sept (13).

8. M Arabpour, A Saghazadeh, N Rezaei. Anti-inflammatory and M2 macrophage polarization-promoting effect of mesenchymal stem cell-derived exosomes. *Int Immunopharmacol*. 2021 Aug;97:107823.

9. W Chen, Y Huang, J Han, L Yu, Y Li, Z Lu, H Li, Z Liu, C Shi, F Duan, Y Xiao. Immunomodulatory effects of mesenchymal stromal cells-derived exosome. *Immunol Res*. 2016 Aug;64(4):831-40.

10. UTT Than, D Guanzon, D Leavesley, T Parker. Association of Extracellular Membrane Vesicles with Cutaneous Would Healing. *Int J Mol Sci*. 2017 May; 18(5): 956.

Chapter 10: EXOSOMES AS LEGITIMATE THERAPY

1. OJ Wouters, M McKee, J Luyten. Estimated Research and Development Investment Needed to Bring a New Medicine to Market, 2009-2018. *JAMA*. 2020;323(9):844-853.

2. Marcia Angell. The Truth About the Drug Companies: How They Deceive Us and What to Do About It. Random House Trade Paperbacks; First Edition (August 9, 2005)

3. (@myriadgenetics. Twitter. June 13, 2023, 6:08AM)

4. https://docs.justia.com/cases/federal/district-courts/california/cacdce/5:2018cv01005/709831/191

5. GA Van Norman. Off-Label Use vs Off-Label Marketing of Drugs. *JACC Basic Transl Sci*. 2023 Feb; 8(2): 224–233.

6. N Farkhad, A Mahmoudi, E Mahdipour. Regenerative therapy by using mesenchymal stem cells-derived exosomes in COVID-19 treatment. The potential role and underlying mechanisms. *Regen Ther*. 2022 Jun; 20: 61–71. 2022 Mar 22.

7. M Sulak, L Fong, K Mika, S Chigurupati, L Yon, N Mongan, RD Emes, VJ Lynch. TP53 copy number expansion is associated with the evolution of increased body size and an enhanced DNA damage response in elephants. *eLife*. 2016; 5: e11994

8. H Hu, Z Ye, Y Qin, X Xu, X Yu, Q Zhuo, S Ji. Mutations in key driver genes of pancreatic cancer: molecularly targeted therapies and other clinical implications. *Acta Pharmacol Sin*. 2021 Nov; 42(11): 1725–1741.

Chapter 11: ANIMAL STUDIES

1. N Mansouri, GR Willis, A Fernandez-Gonzalez, M Reis, S Nassiri, SA Mitsialis, S Kourembanas. Mesenchymal stromal cell exosomes prevent and revert experimental pulmonary fibrosis through modulation of monocyte phenotypes. *JCI Insight*. 2019 Nov 1;4(21):e128060.

2. GR Willis, A Fernandez-Gonzalez, J Anastas, SH Vitali, X Liu, M Ericsson, A Kwong, S A Mitsialis, S Kourembanas. Mesenchymal Stromal Cell Exosomes Ameliorate Experimental Bronchopulmonary Dysplasia and Restore Lung Function through Macrophage Immunomodulation. *Am J Respir Crit Care Med*. 2018 Jan 1;197(1):104-116.

3. E Delavogia, DP Ntentakis, JA Cortinas, A Fernandez-Gonzalez, SA Mitsialis, S Kourembanas. Mesenchymal

Stromal/Stem Cell Extracellular Vesicles and Perinatal Injury: One Formula for Many Diseases. *Stem Cells*, Volume 40, Issue 11, November 2022, Pages 991–1007.

4. SY Ahn, DK Sung, YE Kim, S Sung, YS Chang, WS Park. Brain-derived neurotropic factor mediates neuroprotection of mesenchymal stem cell-derived extracellular vesicles against severe intraventricular hemorrhage in newborn rats. *Stem Cells Translational Medicine*, Volume 10, Issue 3, March 2021, Pages 374–384.

5. C Liu, TH Yang, HD Li, GZ Li, J Liang, P Wang. Exosomes from bone marrow mesenchymal stem cells are a potential treatment for ischemic stroke. *Neural Regen Res*. 2023 Oct; 18(10): 2246–2251.

6. Yan-li Zheng, W Wang, P Cai, F Zheng, Y Zhou, M Li, J Du, S Lin, H Lin. Stem cell-derived exosomes in the treatment of acute myocardial infarction in preclinical animal models: a meta-analysis of randomized controlled trials. *Stem Cell Research & Therapy* volume 13, Article number: 151 (2022).

7. WJ Fan, D Liu, LY Pan, WY Wang, YL Ding, YY Zhang, RX Ye, Y Zhou. SB An, WF Xiao. Exosomes in osteoarthritis: Updated insights on pathogenesis, diagnosis, and treatment. *Front Cell Dev Biol*. 2022; 10: 949690.

8. Yi Jin, Min Xu, Hai Zhu, Chen Dong, Juan Ji, Yake Liu, Aidong Deng, Zhifeng Gu. Therapeutic effects of bone marrow mesenchymal stem cells-derived exosomes on osteoarthritis. *J Cell Mol Med*. 2021 Oct; 25(19): 9281–9294.

Chapter 12: ANECDOTES IN MSK (MUSCULOSKELETAL) PROBLEMS

1. (adapted from) E Makris, P Hadidi, K Athanasiou. The knee meniscus: structure-function, pathophysiology, current repair techniques, and prospects for regeneration. *Biomaterials*. 2011 Oct; 32(30):7411-31.

2. H Asahara, M Inui, M Lotz, Tendons and Ligaments: Connecting Developmental Biology to Musculoskeletal Disease Pathogenesis. *J Bone Min Research*. 2017 June 16: 1-10.

3. https://tinyurl.com/exoblog12

4. CY Li, K Chung, O Ali, N Chung, C Li. Literature review of the causes of pain following total knee replacement surgery: prosthesis, inflammation and arthrofibrosis. *EFORT Open Rev*. 2020 Sep; 5(9): 534–543.

Chapter 13: ANECDOTES IN CARDIOVASCULAR TREATMENTS

1. https://commons.wikimedia.org/wiki/File:Renin-angiotensin-aldosterone_system.png

2. Kurzon (own work 22 Feb 2014). https://en.wikipedia.org/wiki/Windkessel_effect

3. Nzietchueng, M Elfarra, J Nloga, C Labat, J P Carteaux, P Maureira, P Lacolley, J P Villemot, A Benetos. Telomere length in vascular tissues from patients with atherosclerotic disease. *J Nutr Health Aging*. 2011 Feb;15(2):153-6.

4. https://www.rechargebiomedical.com/exosomes-blog-31-leg-swelling/

5. https://www.rechargebiomedical.com/webinar-10-stasis-dermatitis/

6. https://tinyurl.com/exoblog35

7. https://www.rechargebiomedical.com/saint-thaddeus-and-his-namesake/

8. JD Anderson, HJ Johansson, CS Graham, M Vesterlund, MT Pham, CS Bramlett, EN Montgomery, MS Mellema, RLBardini, Z Contreras, M Hoon, G Bauer, KD Fink, B Fury, KJ Hendrix, F Chedin, S El-Andaloussi, B Hwang, MS Mulligan, J Lehtiö, JA Nolta. Comprehensive Proteomic Analysis of Mesenchymal Stem Cell Exosomes Reveals Modulation of

Angiogenesis via Nuclear Factor-KappaB Signaling. *Stem Cells* (Dayton, Ohio), 19 Feb 2016, 34(3):601-613.

9. M Marçola, C Rodrigues. Endothelial Progenitor Cells in Tumor Angiogenesis: Another Brick in the Wall. *Stem Cells Int.* 2015; 2015: 832649.

Chapter 14: ANECDOTES IN NEUROLOGY

1. GS Kote, A Bhat, Thajuddeen K, M Ismail, A Gupta. Peripheral Insensate Neuropathy-Is Height a Risk Factor? *J Clin Diagn Res.* 2013 Feb; 7(2): 296–301.

2. RW Guillery. Observations of synaptic structures: origins of the neuron doctrine and its current status. *Philos Trans R Soc Lond B Biol Sci.* 2005 Jun 29;360(1458):1281-307.

3. S Tuncdemir, C Lacefield, R Hen. Contributions of adult neurogenesis to dentate gyrus network activity and computations. *Behav Brain Res.* 2019 Nov 18; 374: 112112.

4. XC Lu, JY Zheng, LJ Tang, BS Huang, K Li, Y Tao, W Yu, RL Zhu, SL, LX Li. MiR-133b Promotes neurite outgrowth by targeting RhoA expression. *Cell Physiol Biochem.* 2015;35(1):246-58.

5. A Viader, LW Chang, T Fahrner, R Nagarajan, J Milbrandt. MicroRNAs modulate Schwann cell response to nerve injury by reinforcing transcriptional silencing of dedifferentiation-related genes. *J Neurosci.* 2011 Nov 30;31(48):17358-69.

6. https://www.rechargebiomedical.com/exosomes-blog-7-nerve-pain-gone/

7. https://www.rechargebiomedical.com/happiness-is-when-you-know-you-made-a-difference/

8. https://www.rechargebiomedical.com/exosomes-32-nerve-regeneration/

9. https://www.rechargebiomedical.com/exosomes-38-bells-facial-nerve-palsy/

10. https://www.rechargebiomedical.com/exosomes-blog-15-face-blindness/

11. https://www.rechargebiomedical.com/exosomes-36-tinnitus/

12. A Colizza, M Ralli, R Turchetta, A Minni, A Greco, M de Vincentiis. Otolaryngology adverse events following COVID-19 vaccines. *Eur Rev Med Pharmacol* Sci. 2022 Jun;26(11):4113-4116.

13. PW Askenase. Recommendation: Treatment of clinical long COVID encephalopathies with nasal administered mesenchymal stromal cell extracellular vesicles. *Nanotechnol.*, 04 October 2022.

Chapter 15: ANECDOTES IN IMMUNE DYSFUNCTION

1. JA Trevino, P Novak. TS-HDS and FGFR3 antibodies in small fiber neuropathy and Dysautonomia. *Muscle Nerve.* 2021 Jul;64(1):70-76.

2. BJ DeOre, KA Tran, AM Andrews, SH Ramirez, PA Galie. SARS-CoV-2 Spike Protein Disrupts Blood-Brain Barrier Integrity via RhoA Activation. *J Neuroimmune Pharmacol.* 2021 Dec;16(4):722-728.

3. https://www.rechargebiomedical.com/webinar-9-leaky-gut/

Chapter 16: OTHER TREATMENT ANECDOTES

1. https://www.rechargebiomedical.com/exosome-blog-13-microneedling-my-mom-with-exosomes/

2. RL Rajendran, P Gangadaran, SS Bak, JM Oh, S Kalimuthu, HW Lee, SH Baek, L Zhu, YK Sung, SY Jeong, SW Lee, J Lee, BC Ahn. Extracellular vesicles derived from MSCs activates dermal papilla cell in vitro and promotes hair follicle conversion from telogen to anagen in mice. *Sci Rep.* 2017; 7: 15560.

3. https://www.rechargebiomedical.com/114-years-young-whats-her-secret/

4. https://www.rechargebiomedical.com/webinar-20-hair-loss/

5. EA Armstrong, P England, ACK Fogarty. Accounting for Women's Orgasm and Sexual Enjoyment in College Hookups and Relationships. *American Sociological Review*. Volume 77, Issue 3.

6. X Ouyang, X Han, Z Chen, J Fang, X Huang, H Wei. MSC-derived exosomes ameliorate erectile dysfunction by alleviation of corpus cavernosum smooth muscle apoptosis in a rat model of cavernous nerve injury. *Stem Cell Res Ther*. 2018 Sep 26;9(1):246.

OTHER WORKS BY THE AUTHOR

Ed Park, MD
Telomere Timebombs: Defusing the Terror of Aging. Los Angeles, CA.
Telomere Timebombs Publishing Inc; 2013.

Ed Park, MD
The Telomere Miracle: Scientific Secrets to Fight Disease, Feel Great, and Turn Back the Clock on Aging Carlsbad, CA. Hay House Publishing Inc; 2018

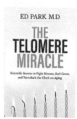

Edward Park and Jove Leksell
Maximum Lifespan: The Graphic Novel
Los Angeles, CA. Pileus Productions; 2010
Download at Amazon.com in 11 languages

Two Houston Film Festival award-winning screenplays:

Edward Park, *Hypatia of Alexandria,* original screenplay

www.tinyurl.com/hypatiascript

Edward Park, *The Brown Dick*, original screenplay

www.tinyurl.com/edbrownscript

ABOUT THE AUTHOR

Dr. Edward H. Park is a medical doctor who practices in five states: California, New York, Florida, Texas, and Hawaii. He received his MD and MPH (Master of Public Health) from Columbia University and his BA and residency training from Harvard University.

He creates blogs at www.rechargebiomedical.com/blogs and videos about aging, telomerase activation, and exosomes, which are available on his YouTube channel "drpark65".

ABOUT THE AUTHOR

Made in the USA
Monee, IL
15 March 2024

54575166R00154